Mastery in Primary Mathematics

Mastery in Primary Mathematics

A Guide for Teachers and Leaders

Tom Garry

BLOOMSBURY EDUCATION
LONDON OXFORD NEW YORK NEW DELHI SYDNEY

BLOOMSBURY EDUCATION
Bloomsbury Publishing Plc
50 Bedford Square, London, WC1B 3DP, UK

BLOOMSBURY, BLOOMSBURY EDUCATION and the Diana logo
are trademarks of Bloomsbury Publishing Plc

First published in Great Britain by Bloomsbury Education

A catalogue record for this book is available from the British Library

ISBN: PB: 978-1-4729-6976-7; eBook: 978-1-4729-6975-0; ePDF: 978-1-4729-6977-4

2 4 6 8 10 9 7 5 3 (paperback)

Typeset by Newgen KnowledgeWorks Pvt. Ltd., Chennai, India
Printed and bound in the UK by CPI Group (UK) Ltd, Croydon CR0 4YY

All papers used by Bloomsbury Publishing Plc are natural, recyclable products from
wood grown in well managed forests. The manufacturing processes conform to the
environmental regulations of the country of origin

To find out more about our authors and books visit www.bloomsbury.com
and sign up for our newsletters

Contents

Acknowledgements

There are a number of people I would like to thank for their support, both in the process of writing this book and over the course of my career more generally.

I would like to thank my colleagues, past and present, who have helped me to develop as a teacher and leader. I've been lucky enough to work with some superb professionals and I owe a great deal to them. I'd particularly like to thank Cath and Tracy for guiding me through the first years of my career and beyond; Cathie and Tim for always providing their wisdom and support, and allowing me the freedom to develop the mathematics teaching at Angel Oak Academy; Matt for sharing his love of both mathematics and teacher education; Saskia and Iona for looking over an early draft of one of my chapters; and all the staff at Angel Oak Academy who make it such a great place to work.

I'd like to thank Lorraine for introducing me to the idea of teaching for mastery, taking me to Singapore to watch some superb teachers in action and teaching me a huge amount about mathematics education. I'd also like to thank Tat, Jonny and Emma for always enjoying a chat about maths.

I've learned from, and been advised by, a great number of people over my career, from the authors and researchers whose work I've read, to the colleagues with whom I work. I'm incredibly grateful for having been exposed to the thoughts and ideas of so many knowledgeable people, and this book is my attempt to pass on some of the wisdom of others. We all stand on the shoulders of giants.

Thanks to Cathie Hewitt for her diamond/square post-it note misconception and to Martin Little for his elephant/mouse analogy – both have made their way into this book. Thank you to Verity, Tom and Sarah who first developed the idea of quadrants at Angel Oak Academy. Also, thank you to Helen Diamond and Harriet Power for their editing, which helped me so much with the process of writing this book and made my thoughts so much clearer on paper.

On a personal note, I'd like to thank my wonderful friends, whom I'm so lucky to have in my life, and also my family, especially my parents, for the love and support that I've always received from them.

Finally, I'd like to thank my incredible wife, Frankie, from the bottom of my heart. She supports me in everything that I do and encouraged me to write this book from day one, even when it meant weekends in, cancelled plans and late nights writing. I quite literally could not have written this book without her love, support and belief, and I owe her all my thanks and love, always.

Introduction

Teaching for mastery is currently in vogue in English schools. Some teachers have known about and used the approach for many years, while for others it's an entirely new way of teaching. For those who were in school-level education more recently, it's likely to be very different to how they were taught themselves. There are ongoing debates about exactly what the term 'mastery' refers to in education, and both the term itself and the approaches that the term entails have been contested over recent years. Although we will look in depth at what we mean when we refer to 'mastery', at its most basic, teaching for mastery is an approach where all learners are expected to reach the same high standard of proficiency, and are effectively supported to do so.

Some see mastery as the latest edu-fad which will be here today and gone tomorrow. I sincerely hope this isn't the case, because I believe that teaching for mastery presents the best solution for ensuring that as many of our pupils as possible learn mathematics successfully. Whereas many non-mastery methods tend to accept that some pupils are simply not good at mathematics, which then results in a lowering of expectations, teaching for mastery involves eschewing this thinking by expecting all pupils to learn the school mathematics curriculum to a high standard, and then working to make this happen.

This success in mathematics for the vast majority of pupils is certainly not happening in this country currently: 76 per cent of pupils reached the expected standard in mathematics in the 2018 KS2 National Curriculum Assessments (SATs). One in four pupils didn't reach the expected standard, and when you take into account that this only required pupils to get just over half marks (61 out of 110, or 55 per cent) this is hardly an impressive state of affairs for mathematics education nationally. Regardless of what your opinions are on SATs, most teachers would agree that a well-educated child should be capable of scoring a high percentage on those tests. Teaching for mastery is a means of making this possibility a reality for almost all children, not just three quarters of them.

This book describes in detail the process of teaching for mastery, outlining the various elements of the approach in the short, medium and long term. It also includes guidance on how you might organise mathematics teaching in your school to ensure that teaching for mastery can take place effectively. This book contains practical advice for everyone, whether you're a teacher teaching a single class or a senior leader working across multiple schools, and it should prove to be as useful to an NQT as it is to an experienced headteacher. It's important to consider how the mastery approach can be implemented at all levels of a school, from the top down and from the bottom up.

This book is aimed at teachers and leaders in *primary schools* – this is where my own expertise lies and I wouldn't presume to make recommendations to my secondary school colleagues. While the approach of teaching for mastery is the same no matter the age of the learners, and much of what this book suggests would also be applicable to secondary schools, the organisation and logistics are different enough to merit separate consideration. There are also features of being a primary teacher that are unique, setting us apart from our subject-specialist colleagues in secondary schools, and I intend to address some of these elements later on in this book.

What I hope to do with this book is to provide a secure starting point for primary teachers who are keen to improve their maths teaching by developing mastery approaches. Part 1 of this book identifies the key elements of teaching for mastery, defines some terms and sets the direction for the rest of the book. Part 2 focuses on the classroom, looking at what teachers can do to implement a mastery approach with their own pupils. Part 3 is aimed at those who oversee mathematics teaching across a whole school or group of schools, focusing on how to lead teaching for mastery and how to create the conditions for the approach to flourish. Teaching for mastery, as a cohesive approach, is unfortunately not something that can be implemented solely by one committed primary teacher. While many elements of unit and lesson design can be taken up and used, a true mastery approach must be implemented across a school with complete support and buy-in from the senior leadership.

Teaching for mastery requires a solid base of mathematical pedagogical content knowledge, but this book is not a place for you to develop that knowledge; it's more about detailing the appropriate structures, behaviours and ways of thinking that will enable you to develop teaching for mastery, either for yourself or across your school. However, I will make suggestions of books and websites where you can go to develop this knowledge in the 'Additional Reading' chapter at the end of the book.

I am fortunate enough to have been both a teacher implementing a mastery approach in my own classroom and a senior leader looking at how the approach can be implemented across a school. I've also worked across a group of schools and seen how the approach can be implemented even more widely. This book is the product of that work, as well as the professional development that I've engaged in over a number of years. I've included things that have gone well, as well as things that haven't, so you can be aware of some of the common pitfalls when implementing the approach.

When I started looking at how to implement mastery in my own school, I relied on the expertise of others, reading from disparate sources and working partly by trial and error. I know that I would have benefitted from a single source to draw from when navigating the difficulties of changing my approach to teaching. While no book can be the sole repository of knowledge on a particular subject, I hope that this one will give you enough of an idea of where to start, as well as indicating where to go for further reading and information. I hope that this book will help you and your colleagues to implement teaching for mastery, and that ultimately it will help all of your pupils to become the excellent mathematicians they deserve to be.

PART 1

A mastery approach

A look at what mastery is, what it isn't, and why we should teach for mastery

1 What is mastery?

Before getting into too much detail about how you can implement a mastery approach in your school or classroom, it's important to spend some time clarifying exactly what we mean by the term 'mastery'. The first thing to bear in mind about mastery is that it is a contested concept. There are fierce battles being waged (online and in person) about what mastery means, and about what does or does not constitute a mastery approach. Firstly, there is the difference in usage between educationalists and lay people, with the word 'mastery' being used widely both within and outside the educational context. Within education, there are those who argue that the teaching for mastery approaches are those formalised by Benjamin Bloom, the American educationalist who is today most famous for his well-known (but often misinterpreted) eponymous taxonomy.

Others argue that teaching for mastery is an approach used in many East Asian education systems, most notably Shanghai and Singapore. These approaches have been the subject of much interest of late in a policy-borrowing context, as the Department for Education (DfE), through the National Centre for Excellence in the Teaching of Mathematics (NCETM), has sought to identify and replicate the practice of maths teaching in highly successful nations as measured by PISA (the Programme for International Student Assessment) and TIMSS (Trends in International Mathematics and Science Study). While there is a great deal of evidence that this type of policy-borrowing is far from as effective or simple as some would want to believe, it was as a result of this interest in the East Asian approach that I was first able to develop my own understanding of teaching for mastery through NCETM's Primary Mastery Specialist programme.

In this book, I hope to recognise the similarities in these two contested versions of mastery and pull them together into a coherent whole, recognising that they have more similarities than they do differences. The definition of mastery below includes elements of both versions, but there is nothing contradictory in their combination. Now, I want to lay out the definition of teaching for mastery around which the remainder of this book is based. Teaching for mastery is an approach which involves the following key elements:

- Identifying what pupils already know about a certain concept.
- Planning the next logical steps in their learning.
- Teaching and assessing in a continual cycle throughout a unit.
- Providing ample opportunities for pupils to develop mathematical fluency and to learn about topics in depth.
- Ensuring a high degree of success for all pupils before moving on to new learning.

Many would argue, as would I, that this simply reflects good maths teaching, already evident in many primary schools across the country. However, in my experience the crucial element missing in many classrooms is the presence of high expectations for *all* pupils. I think this is, in part, a cultural problem, as many people in the UK hold the view that maths is something that you're either good at or you're not. Indeed, while I have never met anyone who is proudly illiterate (although I'm sure that such people exist), I have met a number of people who are proudly innumerate. The idea that it's somehow acceptable to be 'bad at mathematics' can be found in many homes and schools across the country.

Why teach for mastery?

The mindset described above acts as a significant disincentive to aiming for high standards for all. If you don't believe someone is capable of doing something, it seems pointless, or even cruel, to make them attempt it. We feel sorry for those pupils who seem unable to do maths, who fail to grasp the basic concepts and who struggle with content that their peers fly through. The common response to this state of affairs is to lower expectations and provide simpler work that these pupils can access, giving them a modicum of success while their peers plough on. After doing this, we are then for some reason surprised when these pupils don't succeed in their future educational experiences. This mindset is summed up by Michael Gerson's phrase 'the soft bigotry of low expectations'.

If we want all children to be successful, we must ensure that all children have the possibility to be successful mathematicians. Capping or diluting the opportunities for children who are slower to grasp mathematical concepts and procedures will not allow them to succeed later. This is obvious, but often ignored nonetheless. The ludicrousness of what usually happens was neatly summed up in a tweet by Solomon Kingsnorth (@solomon_teach):[1]

'Year 1: differentiate 3 ways please

Year 2: differentiate 3 ways please

Year 3: differentiate 3 ways please

Year 4: differentiate 3 ways please

Year 5: differentiate 3 ways please

Year 6: make them all pass the same test please'

During my teacher training, I was taught that you should split a class into groups based on their mathematical attainment, and then teach each group accordingly: easier work for lower-attaining children and more interesting, rich tasks for high-attaining children. The lesson and learning objective would supposedly be the same for each group, but the different groups would take the learning to different levels. When taken with the belief that a child's attainment reflected what they were capable of, this approach made sense. We all remember those children from our own school days who didn't immediately grasp the mathematical concept that they were taught. Often labelled as 'low ability' and euphemistically placed in the 'triangle' group in primary schools, these children seemed unable to cope with even the most basic maths.

However, when you realise that all pupils are capable of learning maths successfully, this course of action is deeply problematic. The fact that many pupils in English schools struggle with the mathematical content that they're taught doesn't show that they're incapable of succeeding; rather, it shows that they've not been taught using an approach that had high expectations of them, and that they were most likely being taught maths for which they weren't yet ready. Teaching for mastery can change this state of affairs.

Teaching for mastery is built on the underlying belief that all children are capable of learning maths and being successful at it when provided with high-quality teaching and sufficient time. While from time to time, we might find ourselves teaching pupils with severe cognitive challenges who may struggle to learn all of the mathematical content expected in primary education, these pupils are few and far between in mainstream schools. For the overwhelming majority of pupils, success in primary mathematics is well within their reach. Belief in this fact is absolutely fundamental to teaching for mastery. Bearing this in mind, it's important to reflect on the disconnect between this reality and the perceptions of a great many people, both within and outside the educational establishment.

Just for a moment, picture a child you teach, have taught or know personally who finds maths difficult. You have to believe that they are as able to achieve success as much as any other child. Without that belief, those children who need the most support will not be successful.

The importance of our attitudes as teachers was neatly encapsulated in a study by Rosenthal and Jacobson (1966).[2] The experimenters tested a group of primary-age pupils and identified 20 per cent of the cohort as being 'ready to bloom' educationally. Teachers were told which pupils in their classes were these 'special' pupils, but the children were not. However, pupils had actually been randomly assigned to the 'ready to bloom' group; the test was unable to identify those 'ready to bloom' and was in fact only an IQ test. Eight months later, the IQs of all the pupils were retested and the 'bloomer' pupils' IQs had increased more than those of the other pupils, to a statistically significant degree. What mattered most was not their academic aptitude, but their teachers' beliefs and assumptions about them as learners, as these beliefs informed the way teachers behaved towards them. Of course, belief in itself isn't enough, but it *is* an essential prerequisite for success.

Time in schools is limited, as all teachers know only too well, and there is an opportunity cost to teaching – whenever we choose to teach something, we are choosing not to teach something else, and the time that we give over to a lesson can never be recouped. Surely, as our time is so precious, if we choose to teach something to our pupils, we want *all* of them to learn it. Artificially capping the mathematical content that some pupils are able to access will not allow this to happen. This will only result in gaps in pupils' mathematical knowledge compared to their peers, the creation of mathematical 'haves' and 'have nots', and will ultimately lead to another generation of pupils (often the most disadvantaged) growing up having to be proud of the paucity of their knowledge so they don't have to admit that their schooling has failed to teach them one of the most important, useful and beautiful disciplines that there is – mathematics.

There is no such thing as a 'maths brain', or a 'non-maths brain'. We must challenge this assumption wherever we find it. No child is born a great mathematician, just as no child is born a concert pianist. Mathematics, like piano playing, must be learned through hard work, diligence and purposeful practice, all under the guidance of expert instructors. Of course, people have predilections and preferences, things that they find easier or harder, but if you are capable of learning, you are capable of learning mathematics. We must embrace this mindset as educators. Only then can we truly start teaching for mastery.

2 Principles of teaching for mastery

In the previous chapter, I identified five key elements of teaching for mastery:

1   Identifying what pupils already know about a certain topic.
2   Planning the next logical steps in their learning.
3   Teaching and assessing in a continual cycle throughout a unit.
4   Providing ample opportunities for children to develop mathematical fluency and to learn about topics in depth.
5   Ensuring a high degree of success for all children before moving on to new learning.

These elements are underpinned by a series of principles that I have laid out below, all of which feed into teaching for mastery.

Believe that mathematicians are made, not born

Underpinning the actual approach of teaching for mastery is the strong belief about mathematics learning that I touched on before, which is that the vast majority of learners are capable of learning any school-level mathematics. Only those with severe learning difficulties may not be able to do so. This simple idea is revolutionary, and flies in the face of what many teachers learn during their teacher training and in their careers. Indeed, many teachers have first-hand experience that seems to disprove the fact that all children can be successful in mathematics – we have all taught pupils who seem unable to grasp what we've wanted them to learn in maths lessons, especially early on in our careers before we may have had the pedagogical knowledge to fully support them. However, this often comes from pupils having missing foundations in their mathematical knowledge, not an inherent lack of ability to grasp the content. If you go back and teach the missing content, the pupil will be able to move on successfully.

Teaching for mastery does not rely on a fixed idea of mathematical achievement, where some children are born mathematicians and others are not. Rather, it suggests that all children (and adults, in fact) can achieve if they are given sufficient high-quality teaching and enough time. This means that all of our pupils can be successful in their mathematical learning, and the burden is placed on us as teachers to ensure that this happens.

Make sure your planning is coherent

Coherence is an important element of mastery. Mathematics is a hierarchical subject, where all learning relies on what has come before. Shaky or absent foundations are one of the most common reasons for pupils failing to grasp mathematical concepts and procedures. For this reason, the sequencing of learning is of utmost importance in teaching for mastery. This is true at all levels: long term across a curriculum, medium term across a unit of work, and short term across and within lessons. Teaching for mastery involves ensuring that the teaching at all three levels is sequenced carefully and deliberately in order to develop mathematical knowledge that can be built upon later.

Plan for pre- and post-unit assessments so you can identify what to teach

Due to the importance of building solid foundations on which new learning can be built, it's crucial to be able to identify what children already know in order to discern what they should be taught next. Teaching for mastery doesn't dictate that certain things must be taught at a certain age or in a certain year group; in fact, if you take into account the hierarchical nature of mathematics, this idea quickly becomes ludicrous. We cannot simply teach a particular unit because the pupils that we're teaching are of a particular age; we must ensure that we're teaching pupils the next coherent step in their journey of mathematical learning, regardless of their age. For this reason, it's essential to assess frequently as part of teaching for mastery.

Initially, it's important to check that children have already learned any prerequisite knowledge that is necessary for subsequent learning. For instance, teaching long multiplication to pupils who haven't yet learned column addition or their multiplication tables is not sensible. This assessment must take place before teaching a new unit, as some pre-teaching may well need to happen as a result. In addition to these assessments, units should end with assessments in order to identify what pupils have learned. Although no pupil (or adult) can ever be said to have truly 'mastered' something, we want our pupils to be highly successful at what we've taught them. Of course, it's important to remember that performance in an assessment directly after pupils have been taught something does not correlate with whether or not the pupils have learned it for the long term, but it's still important that we assess performance initially.

Don't be tempted to rush on to new learning after a little initial success

Teaching for mastery aims to build deep, sustainable learning. 'Depth' is a word often used in discussions around teaching for mastery. I will look at what we mean when we refer to 'depth' in a later chapter, but a key element of teaching for depth is that we don't allow ourselves to be satisfied with early success at the basics. This was a pitfall I experienced early in my career, witnessing a little success and then moving on to the next lesson or unit. This approach must be avoided. We must design units and lessons that include a variety of activities which allow pupils to explore a wide range of questions rooted in the same mathematical content. Success in the basics is important, but it is no way near enough.

Ensure that pupils achieve a high success rate in what you teach them

This idea can be found in Barak Rosenshine's brilliant *Principles of Instruction*,[3] which I highly recommend if you haven't already read it. A key element of teaching for mastery is ensuring that learners experience high levels of success, both in terms of the basics as well as in the more complex work. We want to ensure that our pupils are confident in the maths they are learning, not just so they *can* do the maths, but so they *can't not* do it. The difference here is that of automaticity gained through practice. For example, while both a novice driver who has recently passed her driving test and an expert driver of twenty years can both be described as 'being able to drive', we can appreciate a huge difference in how they do this. The novice will drive effortfully, thinking about every action and decision consciously, whereas the expert won't have to think about many of these things – they seem to happen automatically. The novice *can* drive; the expert *can't not* drive. This doesn't happen by accident. It happens through a great deal of deliberate practice, guided at first but gradually moving towards independence. This must be how we structure learning for all pupils in mathematics.

Avoid content coverage for its own sake

In many schools, both the 'what' and the 'when' of maths teaching is led by coverage. Teachers are often given a series of mathematical units containing a set amount of content that should be taught over the course of the school year. This content is typically presented as being the appropriate mathematical content that should be covered by that year group. It is then envisaged that the teacher's job is to ensure that all of this content is taught to the pupils. This coverage-focused approach is dominated by discussions of 'getting behind', having to 'catch up' and trying to be 'at the right place' at a certain point in the year. At the end of the year, the teachers who have covered all of their content are able to pat themselves on the back, safe in the knowledge that they've taught what was expected of them. Coverage is the warm safety blanket in which we can wrap ourselves to convince us that we're doing a good job. This approach is a dangerous one.

Firstly, as discussed above, the content that we teach should be led by what our pupils already know. Different groups of pupils will be at different stages in their mathematical learning. There is nothing wrong with having a suggested scheme of work for a particular year group as long as you are clear that this is an ideal scenario to aim for, that it will not be right for any real group of pupils, and that it might have to be adapted or abandoned to meet the needs of the pupils you teach. Assessment will direct you towards what you should teach next, not an idealised curriculum map.

Secondly, different groups of pupils learn at different rates, and so you must tailor the speed at which you progress through your planned learning for your particular cohort of pupils. This may mean that you don't cover everything you're supposed to cover over a year, but this responsiveness is important. Rather than concerning yourself with what you have taught, you should instead focus on what your pupils have learned, and not move on simply because your yearly overview tells you to.

This approach sounds obvious but when working in schools, one of the most common questions that teachers ask me is: what if I don't cover everything that I'm supposed to? The answer is always the same: be more concerned about whether your pupils have learned what they are supposed to. Teaching something does not necessarily mean that pupils have learned it, and coverage is useless if pupils are not learning. Of course, we must have high expectations of what our pupils will learn in a given amount of time, and of course we must map out our mathematics lesson time across the year, but coverage must be our servant rather than our master.

Intervene when pupils require more support

A final principle which is an important part of teaching for mastery is the idea of intervention. No matter how well pupils are taught, it's inevitable that they'll learn at different rates at different times. Every child has a different set of mathematical knowledge in their head, different links between that knowledge and subtly different ways of thinking about the maths they are learning. Of course, we take this into account in our teaching and design our units and lessons accordingly, but the fact remains that some pupils will need more time and instruction to learn what we want them to learn. This means that pupils who grasp the learning more slowly will need additional support and intervention, and you should have systems in place to allow such interventions to take place. There are two different forms of intervention that I'm going to discuss: 'keep-up' interventions and 'catch-up' interventions. They will both be covered in Chapter 15.

A note on setting versus mixed-ability teaching

One aspect of recent discussions around mastery that has proved to be particularly contentious is the notion of whether maths should be set by ability or taught in mixed-ability classes. The argument for mixed-ability teaching tends to run something like this: as teaching for mastery aims to get all pupils to the same point, and as most pupils should move through the curriculum at broadly the same pace (according to the National Curriculum), setting and streaming should not be necessary. Indeed, setting and streaming will work contrary to these goals, as higher sets will move more quickly and this will create a gap between groups. Children who struggle to learn maths are also robbed of the positive role models and examples of high-quality mathematical working evidenced by their top-set peers. Furthermore, setting sends the message that some children are less capable of learning mathematics, and this leads to teachers having lower expectations for pupils in lower sets, thus stunting the performance of those in lower sets.

The counter-argument, that setting by ability is permissible – even desirable – when teaching for mastery, makes the following points: firstly, teaching for mastery requires pupils to be at a similar level of mathematical competence. Teaching a group of pupils the same mathematical concepts assumes they have roughly the same foundation of knowledge on which to build. This creates the need to set or stream as it's not realistic for teachers to teach the same content to pupils with very different foundations of knowledge. In fact, teaching in mixed-ability classes can end up being setting in disguise if different children end up completing different work to manage the spread of attainment. This is something that commonly happens in primary schools, especially in those schools where there is not the space or staff to set pupils. Furthermore, it is not the job of high-attaining pupils to be role models for their peers, it is the job of teachers to ensure that all pupils are exposed to high-quality mathematical thinking. Also, setting allows those pupils in bottom sets to receive the tailored support which they need to help them to catch up to their peers.

I think that elements of each argument are compelling. For instance, take a new cohort of Year 7 pupils in a large, urban secondary school. There will be pupils from several different primary schools, representing a broad attainment range, who have been subject to vastly different teaching methods and a plethora of varied language use, models and explanations. Within such a cohort, there will be some pupils capable of gaining a number of marks on a maths GCSE paper, others to whom much of the KS2 maths assessments would represent little more than gobbledygook, and everything else in between. To then take a random group of 30 of those pupils, put them into a class and ask a teacher to teach them the same mathematical concepts is clearly not sensible. Conversely, making the decision to put pupils into sets in Year 1, as some schools do, seems rather early to be able to accurately identify pupils with similar levels of prior knowledge, especially as the attainment gap will be smaller (although still sadly present) at this age.

As this book is aimed at primary schools, I would make the following suggestion: set pupils where necessary but err towards mixed-ability teaching. I'd argue that teaching in sets tends to create gaps between different groups of pupils, and that our role of getting all our pupils to a high standard of mathematical aptitude could be hampered by this. If your school currently sets throughout, I strongly suggest that you try starting mixed-ability teaching at the bottom of the school, starting with a cohort in the Early Years or Year 1. Then, as these pupils proceed up the school, it's more likely they'll be able to remain in mixed-ability groups.

With other year groups, teachers and leaders should use their professional judgement to decide whether the gap is too big to sensibly allow mixed-ability groups. If this is the case in some year groups, setting should be considered. This will be more likely to be needed further up the school, especially if different groups of pupils have been regularly given different work in maths lessons, whether in separate sets or in different groups within the same class. It's also possible to opt for a hybrid method, using part setting and part mixed-ability. This involves taking out those pupils who have significant gaps in their knowledge and teaching them separately, but keeping the rest of the pupils together in mixed-ability groups. This allows the children who are behind to receive high-quality, targeted instruction designed to close the gaps in learning, but keeps the rest of the pupils mixed, avoiding the creation of further gaps. However, this may be a luxury not possible in many schools.

Case study: ability grouping

At a school where I was maths subject lead, we took a mixed approach to setting. When we first implemented teaching for mastery, we were keen to introduce mixed-ability teaching but were aware of the gaps in learning that existed in many year groups, especially further up the school. We decided that we would be able to teach Years 1–3 in mixed-ability groups, but that Years 4–6 would still require setting due to the existing gaps in their knowledge. We proceeded in this way, and each year we removed setting in one additional year group.

Today, the school still uses a mixed approach to setting, with sets used in Year 6 while other year groups are taught in mixed-ability classes. Year 6 pupils with significant gaps in their learning are taught in a very small group (around six pupils in a cohort of 60) by an experienced teacher. The small size of this group, along with considerable additional interventions, ensures that they have the focused support needed to catch up with their peers. The rest of the Year 6 cohort are taught in larger sets. It remains to be seen whether the school will continue to set Year 6 in future years. Each year, the new Year 6 cohort is coming through with fewer gaps and more knowledge than the previous one, so it may be possible to move away from setting at some point. Having said that, it is always best to set children if that is what will allow them to learn the most. Having pupils with a wide range of attainment in the same class makes teaching for mastery very difficult.

3 Teaching mathematics in the primary school

While teaching for mastery is an approach that can be used effectively with learners of any age, there are aspects of both primary teachers and primary pupils which set them apart from secondary teachers and pupils, and this will impact the way in which maths is taught and learnt. For that reason, I have included a brief discussion of these elements below.

The primary maths teacher

This book is primarily aimed at teachers and school leaders working within primary education. Primary and secondary schools are set up differently, despite having the same broad role of educating children. While the secondary-education paradigm is built around a core of subject specificity and teachers with a great deal of subject expertise, primary education is built on a foundation of generalisation.

The reasons behind this primary-generalist/secondary-specialist dichotomy are varied. Perhaps those with more advanced qualifications are drawn to the 'meatier' role of secondary education where they will be teaching their subject to a higher level; perhaps those with poorer subject knowledge who wish to teach feel that deep subject knowledge is less important in the primary sector; perhaps there are simply not enough subject specialists to teach in both primary and secondary schools. Whatever the reasons, though, it seems that there is little incentive for those prospective teachers with deep subject knowledge to take the path which leads to the primary classroom.

As things stand in England, then, being a primary teacher pretty much equates to being a generalist: the majority of teachers are expected to deliver the entire primary curriculum, except for the odd subject – perhaps PE, art, music or foreign languages, which may be taught by subject specialists depending on the school. In fact, it's interesting to note that we accept that some subjects require specialist knowledge on the part of teachers, but we don't tend to feel the same for our 'core' subjects of English, maths and science. Many of my friends would quite rightly laugh at the idea that I could teach pupils to play football, and no one would suggest that I should teach pupils Mandarin when I am, as yet, unable to speak or understand it. However, we have no problem with allowing a great number of teachers with little deep subject knowledge to teach maths to primary-age pupils.

Perhaps this stems from the idea that those entering the profession are functionally numerate. Graduates, as a rule, can read, write and have enough knowledge of maths to have at least achieved a reasonable grade at GCSE. We tend to think that this, along with passing the professional skills tests, is enough. I don't think it is enough. This way of thinking vastly underestimates the knowledge necessary to teach maths (or any subject) effectively. Being able to do the calculations and get the answers right is not enough; it's only the beginning. The depth of understanding needed to teach a subject as complex and beautiful as maths must not be underestimated.

So, as we have seen, although there are some English, maths and science specialists in the primary system, they are generally few and far between. Generally speaking, a primary teacher is expected to have a broad subject knowledge base, but this knowledge is typically shallow. We primary teachers are the proverbial 'jack-of-all-trades', trained to give pupils a solid foundation in all subjects across the curriculum. But, of course, a jack-of-all-trades is a master of none. And this represents a problem. In fact, I would say that it is deeply problematic. The reason for this is the direct link between subject-specific knowledge and effectiveness. But before we can investigate this further we must first break down what we mean by subject knowledge in the context of maths teaching.

Firstly, a teacher must have mathematical content knowledge. This is knowledge of a subject that is general, in that any person on the street may have such knowledge. Content knowledge is certainly not specific to teachers. Most adults in this country have mathematical content knowledge which will range from the very basic – for someone who was unable to pass a mathematics GCSE, for example – to the very deep – for someone with a PhD in mathematics, perhaps. However, what these vastly varying forms of content knowledge have in common is the fact that they are personal; that is, they don't relate to the transmission of knowledge to anyone else, only how the information is understood by the individual. A person's content knowledge is organised (or disorganised) in a way that makes sense to each individual, but not necessarily to anyone else.

Secondly, teachers will have pedagogical knowledge. This is knowledge concerned with how to teach, how pupils learn, and how to question, assess, check for understanding and the myriad other things that teachers do as a matter of course in their classrooms. This knowledge is specific to teachers and is not held by the general public except in a very general sense. To begin with it may be learned during initial teacher training, depending on the length and nature of the training, and will build up over the course of a career.

Finally, we come on to pedagogical content knowledge (PCK). This knowledge can be found at the nexus of content knowledge and pedagogical knowledge, and essentially involves all the knowledge of how to teach others the content of a specific subject. It includes elements such as knowledge of how to sequence learning, what questions to ask, what misconceptions learners are likely to harbour, what mistakes they are likely to make, what different ways there are of representing concepts, and much more. This is the knowledge that is arguably the most important for teachers, but crucially, having attained a certain level of content knowledge – being able to do the maths for yourself – does not correlate with having good PCK. This is why we must not presume that meeting the requirements to enter the profession – a good GCSE and a passed skills test – will equip us to teach mathematics effectively. Indeed, it is just the beginning of a journey towards expertise in teaching.

There is a significant evidence base that demonstrates the importance of teacher subject knowledge (particularly PCK) to the effectiveness of teaching. For example, the Sutton Trust report *What Makes Great Teaching?* identified six variables that affected pupil outcomes and made an assessment of the evidence base for each variable.[4] Two variables were identified as having the greatest evidence base for having a direct impact on pupil outcomes: the 'quality of instruction' and '(pedagogical) content knowledge'. While both of these variables are dependent on actual classroom experience, new teachers can be supported through significant subject-specific training. This is particularly true of pedagogical content knowledge. However, initial teacher training (ITT) in England, as it is currently stands, does not generally provide trainee primary teachers with anything like the level of training required to have a significant impact on their PCK. This is in part due to the fragmentation of the ITT system.

The wide variety of routes into teaching and the lack of a coherent, nationally agreed curriculum for ITT or NQT training mean that the vast majority of primary teachers are not equipped to teach maths (or indeed any subject) as effectively as they could. While new teachers will almost always be less effective than more experienced teachers, it doesn't seem like the current system does enough to support teachers in developing expertise in the classroom, especially at the start of their careers. I would argue that we currently have a system where many primary teachers, through lack of training, are being sent into schools without the knowledge required to be effective teachers of mathematics.

Some primary teachers will be lucky. They'll have been taught well at school, and will see maths as important, useful, fascinating and even beautiful. They'll have been trained at ITT institutions with coherent syllabi, and will have learned from lecturers and trainers who have passed on the requisite knowledge to teach maths effectively. They'll have gone on to teach at schools with expert subject leads who have the time to develop and support their teachers. These schools will have well-planned, regular professional development on mathematics PCK. Other teachers will not be so lucky.

Of course, it's not all down to luck. Some teachers will actively read around the subjects they teach and question their practice. Platforms such as Twitter provide a useful (albeit argumentative) forum for the sharing of ideas. Many teachers put their heads above the parapet and share what they do in blogs or articles. The subject associations provide a great deal of subject-specific expertise for those teachers who seek it. There are also a number of excellent books available to support primary teachers. However, it's not always easy to know what's out there, especially when you are in the situation of being a primary teacher with several subjects to plan and teach. This book is not a subject knowledge guide, but I hope it will make you aware of the importance of strong mathematical PCK for primary teachers, and that it will point you in the right direction to help you develop this over your career.

The primary mathematics learner

Primary pupils start school with varying amounts of prior knowledge and experience, and different likes, dislikes and proclivities. We know there can be wide gaps in pupils' knowledge on starting primary school. This fact is brought sharply into relief by some research from the United States. A study by Griffin, Case and Siegler (1994), cited in Gersten et al. (2005),[5] found that, when asked questions such as 'Which number is bigger, five or four?', the ability of pupils in kindergarten to answer correctly was hugely influenced by parental income: pupils with a high socioeconomic status could answer this sort of question correctly 96 per cent of the time, whereas pupils with a low socioeconomic status only answered correctly 18 per cent of the time. This is the gap that can exist before children have any formal maths teaching at school. Regardless of any difference in knowledge that our pupils have when they start primary school though, they all have something in common – they are all novice learners.

This fact has implications for how we teach our pupils, who will gradually move from being more novice to being relatively more expert. This process will continue for their entire experience of learning maths. The point at which someone can be thought of as an 'expert' learner is probably moot – it's more of a relative term than an absolute one – but we can safely say that, in primary school, even with our highest-attaining pupils at the top of Key Stage 2 we are always dealing with novice learners.

I was often told during my teacher training that children should not be taught directly; rather, they should be encouraged to explore, to investigate and to discover. I rarely questioned this at the time or in my first years of teaching. This view of teaching is appealing, as experts in many other domains explore, investigate and discover on a regular basis as an integral part of what they do. However, novice learners don't have the same knowledge as experts, and so teaching them in this way is often far less effective than approaches involving more direct instruction, which provide children with more guidance during learning.

Therefore, when we are teaching novice learners in primary schools we must ensure that our teaching is direct and clearly guided. This is what will allow our pupils to learn most efficiently. Kirschner, Sweller and Clark make this point eloquently in their paper *Why Minimal Guidance During Instruction Does Not Work*.[6] David Didau's book *Making Kids Cleverer* makes the same point,[7] as have many other teachers and education researchers. While this is a point that has been debated long and hard, I've learned the hard way that learning mathematics through discovery almost never works in the primary classroom, and I would advocate using the most efficient method of teaching – direct instruction – because the pupils that we teach are not yet experts. Our job is to set them on the path to expertise as quickly and efficiently as we can.

4 Glossary of key terms

As is true in many areas, disagreements about the meaning of words are common in discussions about education. Semantics are important. I'm therefore going to cover the definitions of some key words and phrases that will be used in the rest of this book. I'll use some of these words in ways that will not be universally understood, and so would like to make my meaning absolutely clear from the outset. Some of you, I'm sure, will disagree with these definitions, but it's important for the purposes of this book that you understand my take on these words and how I arrived at these definitions.

Learning: 'a change in long-term memory'

This is Kirschner, Sweller and Clark's definition of learning.[8] When I first read this, something in me resisted it. Perhaps it felt too simplistic. However, the more I thought about it, the more it made sense. For something to be learned, it must be remembered in a lasting way. As has been discussed by many other writers, there are logical implications to this definition. For example, learning is invisible; we cannot see it happening in lessons. We can see pupils answer questions and engage in tasks either successfully or not, but we can't see them learn. Another implication is that learning cannot be said to take place in a single lesson, but rather over time. Performance – correct answers or success in a particular lesson – is not the same as learning. This is not, of course, a flawless definition, and it does depend on our understanding of other terms. However, I think this is a very useful working definition, as it reminds us that learning builds up slowly over time and that it must have longevity.

Knowledge: information, both declarative and procedural, stored in long-term memory

This book isn't an epistemological text and I won't go down the route of saying that knowledge must only be a justified true belief. For the purposes of this book, let's define knowledge as information stored in the long-term memory. This information can be true or false but if it's remembered, then it's knowledge. Indeed, dealing with incorrect knowledge is an incredibly important part of teaching – we design learning to avoid misconceptions from forming and we intervene to deal with misconceptions which already exist. Knowledge, as it's referred to in this book, can be sub-divided into two types: declarative (propositional knowledge) and procedural (non-propositional knowledge).

Declarative knowledge can be thought of as facts stored in the long-term memory. It is knowing 'that'. For example, I know that $7 \times 8 = 56$, that London is the capital of the UK and that *ayuntamiento* is the Spanish word for town hall. Procedural knowledge, as the name suggests, can be thought of as procedures and routines. It is knowing 'how'. For example, I know how to calculate 78×56, how to drive around London and how to ask someone for the directions to the town hall when I'm visiting Spain.

Many people would refer to procedural knowledge as 'skills'. While either term is fine, I prefer the former term, as it serves as a reminder that procedural knowledge is still a kind of knowledge and is still stored in the long-term memory. It's not something entirely separate.

Understanding: 'the gradual acquisition and mental organisation of knowledge'

The definition that I've used for understanding comes from a quote on the subject by Greg Ashman: 'Understanding is not a miraculous threshold that we cross once. It is a gradual, liminal accumulation and reordering of knowledge.'[9] For some time, I believed that my goal as a teacher was to teach my pupils to 'understand' what they were learning. I never questioned this proposition, as it seemed self-evident: of course I must get my pupils to understand! The problem was that I could never really put my finger on what understanding meant, and so I didn't really know how to teach novices to understand things. That's because my thinking was based upon a fundamental misunderstanding of what this word meant.

I now believe that the word 'understanding' simply defines a relative position on the imaginary continuum from complete ignorance to complete mastery. You can have greater or lesser understanding than someone else in a particular domain of knowledge, but no one achieves complete understanding of anything. When a pupil seems to understand something, what we are witnessing is a rich, well-ordered schema, a web of knowledge that has been built up over time. Someone who seems to understand something simply has a lot of well-organised knowledge, nothing more, nothing less. Children who seem to lack understanding typically have a lack of knowledge, or insufficiently well-ordered links between knowledge.

Occasionally, a pupil may seem to suddenly understand a concept or idea – the proverbial lightbulb moment. However, this is not some kind of quantum leap from ignorance to understanding; rather, it's the final piece of a jigsaw slotting neatly into place. A huge amount of background knowledge has been built up and a single new piece of information then draws this together. A key implication of this is that there isn't a different, superior method of teaching for understanding. The more we teach our pupils about a certain concept, the more they will understand it. There are ways of increasing the knowledge that pupils have about a particular concept in a deep and systematic way – for example, one key method is through the use of variation theory – but in a nutshell, we move pupils towards greater understanding as we teach them more knowledge.

Representation: a visual or linguistic model to demonstrate an abstract concept in a concrete way

Representations are a crucial part of maths teaching. As mathematics is a mostly abstract endeavour, we use a variety of representations to help pupils to make sense of abstract concepts. There are several different ways in which we can represent abstract mathematics. Concrete (physical manipulatives) and pictorial (images) are two well-known forms of representation which are used alongside abstract maths, but other forms of representation include language and situational contexts. These representations are essential to developing pupils' knowledge of a concept.

Learning step: a single unit of mathematical content to be taught which is as small and precise as practically possible

Later in this book we'll consider why it's important to think and structure our teaching in terms of learning steps, rather than lessons. Learning steps are the key units of planning and teaching maths. When we plan a series of lessons, we break up the mathematical content into learning steps which we then deliver sequentially. A learning step is not the same as a lesson. A learning step is a measure of mathematical content, whereas a lesson is a measure of time. A lesson is simply a convenient unit into which we divide our time as teachers, whereas a learning step is a coherent unit of mathematical content to be learned. Learning steps are thus what you should focus on when planning the maths, although lessons will be the focus when planning your time.

Instructional sequence: a series of linked learning steps about a particular area of mathematics

An instructional sequence can be thought of as a mathematical unit made up of a number of smaller learning steps. As with a learning step, however, the focus is on content to be taught rather than time. I also like the temporal implications of the word 'sequence', forcing us to think about how our learning steps work as part of a coherent whole. There is no set number of learning steps that would make up an instructional sequence – it depends on a number of factors such as the area of mathematics covered and pupils' prior knowledge and level of expertise.

Activity: a series of questions or problems in a lesson that are designed by the teacher and answered individually by pupils

The activities that we plan assess pupils' knowledge of the learning step that is currently being taught. Activities could take the form of a worksheet with multiple questions, a page from a textbook or a single problem for pupils to solve, depending on the learning step and other factors.

PART 2

Teaching for mastery

A look at how we teach for mastery in the classroom, considering the design and delivery of instructional sequences (the medium term), learning steps (the short term) and activities (what our pupils do in lessons)

Section 1 Instructional sequence design and delivery

The following chapters will consider how to design and deliver an instructional sequence – a coherent set of mathematical learning steps within a particular mathematical domain. When following a mastery approach, the maths curriculum that a school plans is broken down into a number of smaller units (instructional sequences) which will run over a series of days and weeks. Each unit is made up of a series of smaller learning steps which will be completed within or across individual lessons (see Figure 1).

An instructional sequence is the most important level of learning design in teaching for mastery. It sets out a series of learning steps on a particular mathematical topic, identifying the starting point and end point of a learning sequence and all of the coherent steps in between. In essence, it captures the sequence of knowledge that we want our pupils to learn. It maps out the route from where their understanding is now to where we want it to be. The idea of coherence is a crucial element of teaching for mastery, and this is true at all levels of planning, from the macro (the curriculum) to the micro (a single learning step). Each step must link clearly to the previous and subsequent steps, to best create a clear narrative that pupils can follow as they progress through the mathematical content in the sequence.

It may seem strange to start with designing an instructional sequence that looks at the medium term rather than thinking about the short or the long term. I've deliberately chosen to start at this level of planning as most classroom teachers don't have any say over the structure of a school's curriculum (although subject leads and senior leaders may do). However, many teachers do have control over their medium-term plans. For this reason, I will start here.

I'm not advocating any particular method of planning; how you choose to actually plan your unit will depend on a number of factors, including your school's expectations, your experience and what materials you are using to support your planning. Some teachers will have to use a particular template, others may use a blank piece of paper and others may have planning provided. Whatever method you use, I'll identify some of the key elements of an instructional sequence that you should try to capture in the planning process.

Before jumping into the planning process, it's important to note that if you're provided with detailed unit plans in your school, you shouldn't simply deliver them exactly as they are. An important element of teaching for mastery – indeed, arguably the *key* point of teaching for mastery – is the process of accurately identifying the prior knowledge of your pupils and then following on from this point in your teaching. This will change year on year, cohort to cohort. The best-produced plan that is written by someone else will not match the needs of your children; it will need careful adaptation and should therefore only be a guide. Also, please bear in mind that there is no such thing as a 'Year 4 plan' or 'Year 4 mathematics'. Even when using a high-quality textbook, you must not simply proceed with the suggested work without being sure that it is at the correct stage of learning for your pupils. They need whatever the next step of mathematical learning is, regardless of their year group.

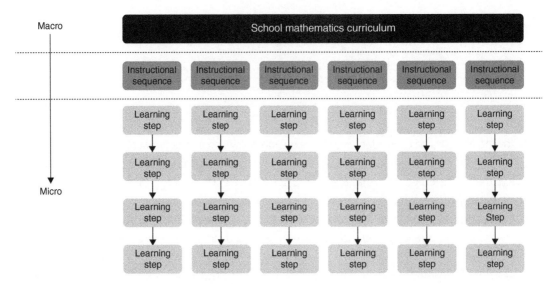

Figure 1

The stages of planning an instructional sequence

There are a number of key stages involved in planning an instructional sequence for your pupils, and these will be outlined in greater detail in the coming chapters. For a particular unit of work, you will need to identify the end goal that you want your pupils to reach and plan backwards from there. For each step, you will have to identify the vocabulary that pupils need to understand and the common misconceptions that pupils are likely to make. You will also need to identify the mathematical representations that you'll use in your teaching, the big ideas and key concepts that will appear in your instructional sequence and the prerequisites necessary for success in the new learning. You will also need to plan tests and quizzes to assess the learning of your pupils as you progress through the learning sequence. After this process, your instructional sequence will be planned. The last chapter in Section 1, 'Delivering an Instructional Sequence', will explain how to put your plan into action. Before that, we'll first look at some of the stages described above in more detail to help you plan your instructional sequences.

5 Planning coherent learning steps

Identifying the learning steps

The first stage in designing an instructional sequence is identifying the learning steps that you need to teach. As a starting point, it's essential to know what children may have learned previously about the area of maths that you are planning to teach. Depending on where you are in the academic year, this prior teaching may have happened in a previous year, but it could also have been taught by you. It's helpful to look at the unit plan from the last time your pupils were taught this particular area of maths. This won't tell you much about what the children have actually learned, of course, but it's useful to know what the intended learning was. As well as looking at previous planning, it's well worth looking at assessment data from previous instructional sequences, as well as any classwork that the pupils have completed (presuming that these are accessible to you).

Once you have a good sense of what your pupils may have been taught before, you can start to develop a tentative idea of what they should be taught next. The most effective way to plan for a new instructional sequence is to leap right to the end of the sequence, asking yourself what it is you want your pupils to know and be able to do by the end of it (see A in Figure 2).

Once you have this idea firmly in mind, you can start working backwards in steps from this imagined end point to where you think your pupils might be now (see B in Figure 2). This process is where the small learning steps come from. Each time, ask yourself this: to be successful with this step, what must pupils know already? And to know *that*, what must pupils have learned beforehand? And so on, until you are back to where you believe your pupils are now.

For instance, if you're planning on teaching your class to calculate with fractions, they might currently know what fractions are as a concept, and be able to find equivalent fractions and compare the relative size of fractions. Your desired end point might be 'to add and subtract unit and non-unit fractions with different denominators, including mixed numbers'. This represents 'A' above, the leap between now and a perceived future state. You would then work backwards from there in small steps, which might include the following:

- Convert improper fractions to mixed numbers
- Subtract with mixed numbers
- Add with mixed numbers
- Convert mixed numbers into improper fractions
- Subtract fractions from whole numbers
- Add fractions to whole numbers
- Subtract fractions with different denominators (bridging 1)
- Add fractions with different denominators (bridging 1)

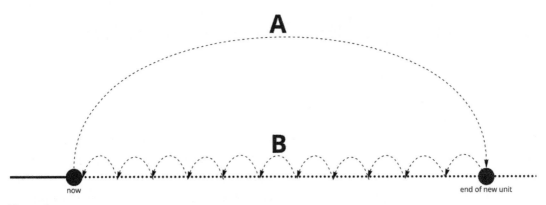

Figure 2

- Subtract fractions with different denominators (within 1)

- Add fractions with different denominators (within 1)

- Find a common denominator between fraction pairs (converting both fractions)

- Find a common denominator between fraction pairs (converting one fraction)

- Subtract fractions with the same denominator (bridging 1)

- Add fractions with the same denominator (bridging 1)

- Subtract fractions with the same denominator (within 1)

- Add fractions with the same denominator (within 1)

- Find pairs of fractions that equal 1

This sequence, running backwards from the final step at the top to the first step at the bottom, represents the coherent sequence of learning steps through which this instructional sequence would progress.

After you've established the order of your learning steps, it's then important to go back and review them. Does the order make sense? Are there any missing steps? Should any of the steps be broken down into smaller steps? This process, best conducted in discussion with colleagues or subject leads, will give you an ordered sequence of learning steps – the skeleton on which the rest of your planning for the instructional sequence will hang. The next step of planning is to identify common misconceptions for each learning step.

Identifying misconceptions

Once you've identified your learning steps, it's important to start fleshing out your plan by considering the misconceptions that your pupils might have for each learning step. Identifying misconceptions, and then teaching in order to correct them or avoid them in the first place, is one of the most important parts of teaching. It's also one of the hardest! Identifying misconceptions is an excellent example of the pedagogical content knowledge that teachers should have in relation to how the mathematical content should be learned. It's worth noting that the ability to identify misconceptions is also affected by 'the curse of knowledge': the more that we know about a particular concept, the harder it can be to understand why others can't grasp it. This is why we need more than just subject knowledge to be good teachers, as we can be blinded by our own expertise.

For each learning step, try to predict some of the key mistakes and misconceptions that your pupils might make. If we stay with the theme of adding and subtracting fractions, one common misconception is that denominators should be added or subtracted as well as the numerators. Once you've identified misconceptions, you'll be able to start considering how you'll teach to avoid or address these misconceptions, preventing pupils from learning something incorrect and correcting those pupils who may already have done so. This might be done through explicit teaching, choosing questions carefully to elicit misconceptions or choosing particular misconceptions to demonstrate some aspect of a concept clearly. Texts specifically addressing misconceptions can be found in the 'Additional Reading' chapter at the end of the book.

After having identified the key misconceptions for each learning step, it's then important to consider the mathematical language that pupils will need to use in lessons to describe and discuss their mathematical learning.

Identifying vocabulary

Language is the stuff of thought. Without having a word for something, it can be very difficult to think about it. It's not impossible, but having the right words makes thought clearer, more concise and more precise. To take a non-mathematical example, think of the word 'schadenfreude'. A loanword from German, schadenfreude refers to the pleasure derived from another's misfortune. Before English speakers began using this word, people no doubt felt schadenfreude, but having a word with such precision of meaning gives the feeling clarity. It also makes discussion of the feeling simpler, and the feeling itself more identifiable. Maths is no different. We want our pupils to think about maths. This is made much easier if children are consistently given the correct vocabulary throughout their time in primary school. It enables them to think and talk with precision and conciseness. There is no agreed age at which the correct names for ideas should be introduced, but a good rule of thumb when introducing a concept, symbol or idea is to name it correctly. It makes things much easier, rather than trying to backpedal and rename ideas in later years.

When planning your learning steps, consider the vocabulary that your pupils will need for each step. If you don't know it yourself, find out. A good-quality mathematical dictionary will never go amiss, but there are also websites such as www.mathsisfun.com which have superb glossaries and explanations. Identify and use the correct vocabulary with your pupils, all the time, no matter their age or the apparent complexity of the vocabulary.

In addition to the use of precise language in lessons, it's useful to identify stem sentences that you could use to help define or explain concepts. These are good for drawing pupils' attention to particular aspects of the learning and they encourage accurate speaking in lessons. These stem sentences generally contain a proposition and a blank space or two which pupils must fill in. In the context of fractions, a useful stem sentence might be:

'In this fraction, the denominator is _____ because the whole is split into _____ equal parts.'

In this example, pupils will initially notice that the denominator always reflects the number of equal parts into which the whole is divided. They will notice this for a specific instance first, such as: 'In this fraction, the denominator is **five** because the whole is split into **five** equal parts.' Repeated use of this stem sentence will start to embed the idea that the denominator is always 'the number of equal parts', and this represents a move from the specific (one fifth is comprised of five equal parts) to the general (one x is comprised of x equal parts). Stem sentences are useful for several reasons: they encourage children to speak in full sentences using the correct vocabulary; they give pupils a structure to guide their thinking; and they lend themselves to making generalisations, where pupils can move from the specific to the general, which is a hugely important element when learning mathematics.

So when planning your learning steps, along with considering any vocabulary that you will use, think about stem sentences that might be helpful in developing your pupils' knowledge of each step. They might not necessarily be useful for all learning steps, but they can be a powerful tool in encouraging purposeful talk in your classrooms and drawing your pupils' attention to key mathematical ideas.

At the end of this process, you will have identified and ordered a series of small, coherent steps which you can guide your pupils through as you teach the instructional sequence. You will also have identified some of the key misconceptions that pupils are likely to make, as well as some of the vocabulary that your pupils will use. This is the skeleton of your instructional sequence. The next step is for you to identify the mathematical representations that will help your pupils to make sense of the maths that you are teaching them.

Planning coherent steps: key points

- Gather as much information as possible about your pupils' prior learning in this area of mathematics. Previous plans, assessment data, pupils' work and discussions with colleagues can all feed into your mental picture of what your pupils already know.

- Work out your ideal end position: what do you want your pupils to know by the end of the sequence?

- Work backwards from this end point in small steps, asking each time: 'To be successful at this step, what must I first teach my pupils to do?'

- Ensure that your learning steps are well broken down and coherently sequenced.

- For each step, identify any misconceptions that pupils could have regarding the learning.

- For each step, identify the vocabulary that pupils will need to know in order to be able to think and talk about the mathematics, including any useful stem sentences.

6 Identifying representations

The value of mathematical representations

Maths is primarily an abstract discipline. It can be represented concretely and can be used to solve real-life problems but it is essentially abstract in itself. David Geary, an evolutionary psychologist, has made the distinction between two types of knowledge: biologically primary knowledge – that which we are evolved to learn simply through interacting with our environments with relative ease – and biologically secondary knowledge – culturally specific knowledge that we have not evolved to learn. Maths can be classed as a biologically secondary endeavour, and thus we generally find it difficult and demanding to learn. Humans evolved in a concrete world, and we more readily understand concrete situations than abstract ones. To support pupils' learning in maths, therefore, we should make use of concrete examples to develop their knowledge of mathematical concepts. As outlined in the glossary, this book defines all of the different ways of presenting maths as 'representations'. Here are the key types of representations:

- **Concrete:** a physical representation that can be touched and manipulated by pupils. Often known as manipulatives. Cuisenaire rods are one example of a concrete representation.
- **Pictorial:** an image, often simplified so that it could potentially represent any number of different things. For example, a picture of a circle could equally represent an apple, a basketball or a cake in a pictorial representation of a problem.
- **Abstract:** a representation using symbolic mathematical notation, such as $3 + 5 = 8$.
- **Contextual:** a representation using a situation that can be described in mathematical terms. For example, 'Frankie has £100 and spends £27.97 on books. How much money does she have left over?'
- **Linguistic:** linguistic representations are important, and often overlooked. We frequently use different language structures to describe abstract maths, and these structures can vary greatly. For example, we could linguistically represent the calculation $88 \div 11$ in a number of ways:
  - What is eighty-eight divided by eleven?
  - How many times does eleven go into eighty-eight?
  - What goes into eighty-eight eleven times?
  - What multiplied by eleven gives eighty-eight?
  - What is eleven times smaller than eighty-eight?
  - Eighty-eight is eleven times larger than what?
  - How many times larger than eleven is eighty-eight?
  - How many times smaller than eighty-eight is eleven?

And so on. Pupils need to understand that these questions all represent the same abstract maths. Learning to recognise, create and move between these multiple representations supports pupils in learning mathematical concepts.

For instance, this is one representation of a particular mathematical idea:

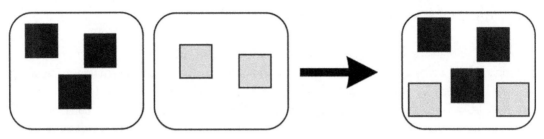

Figure 3

This example is a pictorial representation. We could represent this in the abstract as 3 + 2 = 5. In the concrete, we might ask pupils to place three toy cars, blocks or counters in a box, add two more and then count the total. A description of that action could serve as a contextualised representation of the situation. Linguistically, we might represent the maths by saying 'three plus two is equal to five' or something more descriptive, such as 'if we have three of something and then add two more, we will have five things in total'.

To show another example, we might want children to be able to solve this calculation:

$$\frac{1}{2} \times \frac{1}{3} =$$

As it is laid out here, this is an abstract representation. It is one that learners struggle to visualise, as multiplying a number by something less than one is not easy to imagine at first. Using representations can help with developing pupils' understanding of what is happening. We could start by altering our language. Rather than saying 'one half times one third', asking 'what is half of one third?' or 'what is one third of one half?' begins to illuminate the situation. In the concrete, we could use Cuisenaire rods:

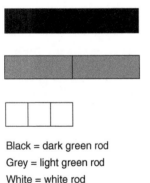

Black = dark green rod
Grey = light green rod
White = white rod

Figure 4

If the dark green rod is 1, then the light green rod represents one half of the whole. The white rod is one third of the light green rod, and so is one third of one half. As six white rods would equal the dark green rod (the whole), we can say that $\frac{1}{2} \times \frac{1}{3} = \frac{1}{6}$.

Pictorially, we could use an array to represent the calculation. For instance, we could start with a 1 x 1 array with an area of 1:

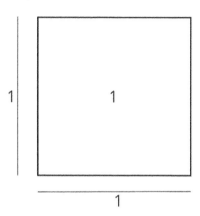

Figure 5

If we then sub-divide one side into two equal parts (halves) and the adjacent side into three equal parts (thirds), we can see that the area of the array where one third and one half intersect has an area which is one sixth the area of the whole:

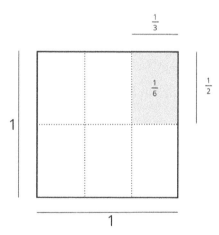

Figure 6

Being able to move between these multiple representations demonstrates a deepening knowledge of the mathematical concept being learned. This will begin to happen as we present children with varying representations of the same mathematical concept, and over time they will begin to use these representations themselves. This will be covered in more depth in Chapter 12 on conceptual variation.

Representations are an important part of maths teaching and using them in your lessons is essential as they give children a way to structure their thinking about abstract mathematical concepts. The visual and linguistic models help children to develop their own mental models which they can then employ when thinking about abstract maths in the future. Representations can be used with all ages of learners and are necessary for all children. The most common misjudgement that I encounter in primary schools, especially in terms of using concrete representations, is that they should only be used with younger pupils (typically Early Years and Key Stage 1), and then only with any older pupils who seem to be struggling to grasp concepts. These representations are necessary for everyone, and all learning sequences should include multiple representations to allow pupils to develop their own mental models.

Identifying representations

To come back to the process of planning, once you've identified your learning steps it's really important to consider how you will represent the maths in each step. The more representations you're able to use, the richer your pupils' knowledge will be, provided they are used well. When designing and delivering individual learning steps, consider how to present the representations that you've selected, as it's important not to simply present several different representations in one go. As part of the planning process, however, it's sufficient to gather as many examples of representations as you can. It's likely that the representations you use will be similar for a number of learning steps. However, it's also likely that you will find some representations to be more useful for some learning steps than others.

When choosing representations it's important not to only choose 'standard' ones with which pupils are familiar; you should ensure that you choose 'non-standard' representations too – ones which will develop your pupils' understanding of a concept. It's also equally important to expose children to 'non-concept' representations – examples which demonstrate what a concept is *not*, as well as what it is. This is an incredibly important part of teaching for mastery, as seeing a wide range of examples and non-examples will develop pupils' knowledge of what a concept is and what it isn't, broadening their knowledge by defining a concept's boundaries. This will be covered in greater depth in the coming chapters on variation.

To identify representations for your instructional sequence, consider each learning step and think of the abstract maths that you'll be teaching in that step. Then, taking into account the different types of representation listed above (concrete, pictorial, linguistic, contextual), consider how you could represent that abstract mathematical concept. Remember there are a huge number of representations that you could use to show any mathematical concept, so it's key to bear in mind what it is you want pupils to learn, as different representations have different strengths and weaknesses. Let's take an example.

If we were teaching an instructional sequence on addition within 20, there are a whole host of representations that we could use. For a calculation such as 8 + 7, we could represent it with dienes, with two sets of counters being combined, with counters in ten frames, or with beads on a bead string (see Figure 7).

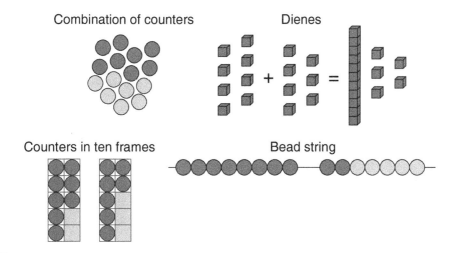

Figure 7

However, these representations are not equally useful. When adding pairs of numbers that will involve changes to multiple place value columns (adding eight and seven will alter both the ones and tens columns, whereas adding two and seven would only alter the ones), a key thing we want pupils to notice is that we can mentally 'make ten' as an interim stage. So, 8 + 7 can be thought of as 8 + 2 + 5, taking two from the seven to 'make ten' with the eight and then adding on what is left (five). The bead string is a very effective method for demonstrating that, as the colour change after each group of ten beads allows you to 'see' the two and the five which make up seven, as they're different colours.

A similar thing can be noticed with the ten frames, where we can see the 'missing' two in the first ten frame, making it easy to visualise two counters from the second ten frame moving across to fill up these spaces. If we contrast this approach to simply using counters, we can see that using counters alone doesn't help pupils to easily see that they can make ten. This type of consideration is essential when selecting the key representations that you will use as you proceed through your instructional sequence.

Once you have identified the representations that you will use, you need to think about when they will be introduced and in what order. This will largely be decided by the order of your learning steps and the key points that you wish to get across at each stage. Remember to make links between different representations, especially when first introducing them to pupils. If a Cuisenaire rod is representing a particular value, say so explicitly. What may seem obvious to us may not be to our pupils. In EYFS and Key Stage 1, where our concrete resources may well be actual objects (pieces of fruit, for example), moving to cubes or counters from the actual objects requires explicit explanation: *'This cube represents a pear, and this cube represents another pear. What could I use to represent an orange?'* The importance of explicitly linking different representations should not be underestimated.

A common misconception in maths teaching is that any mathematical concept should be represented in three distinct phases, first in the concrete, then in the pictorial and finally in the abstract. This is not necessarily the case, although it is an understandable mistake to make. As we have seen, maths is an abstract subject – possibly the most abstract endeavour that humans engage in – and we want pupils to ultimately work in abstract terms. However, the human brain doesn't easily deal with abstractions and needs concrete examples to make sense of them.

Therefore, when first introducing a concept, concrete examples are very helpful in developing understanding. Over the course of learning about a concept, the concrete will be needed less frequently, being replaced by more pictorial and abstract representations, with the majority of representations being abstract ones once a concept is more securely understood. It's important to see this as a gradual fading from concrete, through pictorial to abstract, with all three types of representation being present all the way through, just in differing proportions. This is different from the 'first concrete, then pictorial, finally abstract' approach as understood by some. It is the links between the different representations that give them their strength, and which allow pupils to learn from them.

Identifying representations: key points

- For each learning step you have planned, consider the representations that you will use in your teaching.

- Ensure you have considered how to represent the maths in all five of the key modes of representation: concrete, pictorial, abstract, contextual and linguistic.

- Gather a wide variety of representations for the learning steps in your instructional sequence.

- Select the representations that will best help you to make your teaching points.

- Make explicit links between representations when you introduce them, ensuring that pupils are secure with each representation that you use.

- Don't think of concrete, pictorial and abstract as three distinct phases that you will move through. Instead, use all three throughout an instructional sequence, but decrease the proportion of concrete representations and increase the proportion of abstract representations as the sequence progresses.

7 Identifying big ideas

Once you've identified the small learning steps that will comprise the skeleton of your instructional sequence, it's just as important to consider the macro level: how does the learning in this unit link to other areas of mathematical learning? What are the overarching ideas and concepts that pupils will come across in this instructional sequence, the ones which they may have encountered before and are likely to encounter again? These key concepts, or big ideas, are central to pupils' understanding of the discipline of mathematics. They are the glue that binds together the subject, even where elements may seem disparate.

You should be aware of these big ideas, as pupils need to be exposed to them explicitly in order for them to make links between different areas of maths. For example, measurement is one strand of the curriculum which may seem to be quite separate from the strand of fractions, decimals and percentages. While it's possible to make surface links between them (one kilometre is five eighths of a mile, for example), certain big ideas link the areas at a much deeper level – the idea of equivalence, for instance. Pupils will learn that it's possible to find a number of fractions that are equal to each other (a half, two quarters, three sixths, etc.) and in the same way, it's possible to find a number of measurements which are equal to each other (1 metre, 1000 millimetres, 0.001 kilometres…). The idea of equivalence fundamentally links these two areas, as well as all areas of maths. Equivalence is one important example of a big idea that we will look at in more detail shortly.

Structuring a maths curriculum by distinct strands is a common and sensible approach – we need to be able to break down a large number of ideas into linked domains. The National Curriculum in England identifies ten such domains:

- Number and place value
- Addition and subtraction
- Multiplication and division
- Fractions, decimals and percentages
- Ratio and proportion
- Algebra
- Measurement
- Geometry – properties of shapes
- Geometry – position and direction
- Statistics

However, this structuring of the curriculum encourages the separation of these domains in the eyes of teachers and pupils, who then consider them as separate entities. While this separation is necessary for sensible organisation, it is the big ideas that pull these strands together into a coherent whole, which help to show how each separate domain is part of the whole of mathematics. If we as teachers are clear about what some of these big mathematical ideas are, we'll be able to draw our pupils' attention to them while we're teaching.

What are the big ideas in mathematics?

Unfortunately, there is no easy answer to this question and no definitive list of mathematical big ideas. As with all such things, there is debate about the relative importance of big ideas, and different experts have differing views on this matter. One of the most well-known lists was compiled by Raymond Charles. His list of 21 big ideas fundamental to elementary and middle school mathematics (the article was originally published in the US) is comprehensive:[10]

1 Numbers

2 The base ten numeration system

3 Equivalence

4 Comparison

5 Operation meanings and relationships

6 Properties

7 Basic facts and algorithms

8 Estimation

9 Patterns

10 Variable

11 Proportionality

12 Relations and functions

13 Equations and inequalities

14 Shapes and solids

15 Orientation and location

16 Transformations

17 Measurement

18 Data collection

19 Data representation

20 Data distribution

21 Chance

In addition to Charles's list, a number of others have published their own take on mathematical big ideas, including Mike Askew[11], Debbie Morgan[12], Nancy Barclay and Alison Barnes[13], as well as others. While there is obviously no 'definitively correct' list, by comparing a variety of examples we can see what the similarities and differences are. Some of the commonalities across multiple lists are instructive. The following ideas occur across multiple lists of big ideas:

- Equivalence
- Pattern
- Proportionality

All three of these ideas are highly important concepts in mathematics that pupils will encounter again and again in their education. Alongside these three crucial big ideas, the following big ideas appear on two of the lists mentioned above and are clearly important ideas for pupils to be exposed to as well:

- Proof
- The 'base ten' place value number system
- Classification
- Comparison
- Proportionality
- Estimation
- The meanings of and relationships between operations and their symbols
- Representation

Let's now look briefly at equivalence as an example of a big idea and consider how it occurs across several different areas of maths.

Equivalence

The idea of equivalence is clearly a crucial concept in maths. The symbol for equivalence, =, is encountered by pupils early in their schooling. Unfortunately, it is often taught poorly, without giving pupils any understanding that the symbol denotes the equality of the two terms it separates. Too often, the equals symbol is implicitly used by teachers to show where to put the solution to a calculation, as in:

$$3 + 2 =$$

The actual meaning of the symbol is too often not referred to. This means that expressions which are not presented in a 'typical' way are initially confusing to many pupils:

$$= 3 + 2$$

$$4 + \quad = 3 + 2$$

To counteract these confusions and misconceptions, it's essential that pupils are taught from the beginning that the equals symbol simply means that the two expressions on each side have an equal value. Visuals such as Figure 8 can help to develop pupils' understanding of this concept. In this figure, the image of the 'less than' symbol uses squares to show that the left side of the symbol is smaller (one square is smaller than five squares), so we write the smaller number to the left of the symbol. The 'greater than' symbol shows the opposite. The central image, the equals symbol, shows that two sides of the symbol are the same (two is equal to two), so the terms on either side of the symbol should be equal. By using the small squares in this way, pupils can see what these symbols represent and why.

Figure 8

As well as explicitly teaching the meaning of the equals symbol, regular exposure to questions where a missing term can be on either the left or right side of the symbol will ensure that pupils know there is no 'right' or 'wrong' way round to write an expression of equality. When reading equations aloud, using the words 'is equal to' for the symbol reiterates the idea that there is no 'right way round' for an equation to be. So, 5 = 9 - 4 should be read as 'five is equal to nine minus four.'

Equivalence is everywhere within the maths curriculum. As well as in the four operations, where equivalence is part and parcel of pupils' learning, equivalence is crucial to pupils' understanding of place value. Knowing that a digit in a place value column is equivalent in value to ten of the same digit in the column to the right (for example where 6,000 = 600 x 10) is central to our pupils' understanding of the number system. Another area where pupils will regularly encounter equivalence is the area of fractions, decimals and percentages. For example, they are taught to find equivalent fractions and so know that $\frac{1}{3}$ is equivalent to $\frac{2}{6}, \frac{3}{9}$ and so on. Visual representations such as Figure 9 are an excellent way to demonstrate this equivalence.

Pupils also learn about equivalence through being taught to convert between fractions, decimals and percentages. For example, pupils learn that $\frac{4}{10}$ is equivalent to 0.4 and 40 per cent.

Beyond number, pupils will also encounter equivalence in other areas of maths:

- In shape, for example, we can have shapes with equivalent areas and volumes but different dimensions, so a 2 x 3 oblong has an area equivalent to a 1 x 6 oblong, and a 4 x 5 x 6 cuboid has a volume equivalent to a 2 x 5 x 12 cuboid.

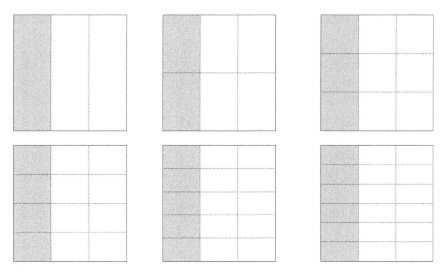

Figure 9

- A shape with lines of symmetry can be divided into equivalent pieces.

- A line bisecting another line creates two pairs of equivalent angles.

- In measurement, 20 kilometres is equivalent to 20,000 metres, 20,000,000 millimetres or 20 hectometres.

A concept which occurs again and again when considering equivalence is the idea of infinity. As numbers are infinite, so too are the number of equivalent expressions for any given number. For example, $2 = 1 + 1, 2 = 0 + 2, 2 = -1 + 3, 2 = -2 + 4$ and so on, ad infinitum. There are an infinite number of fractions which are equivalent to $\frac{1}{2}$, or to any given fraction. Similarly, there are an infinite number of triangles with an area of 25 cm², or indeed any other shape and any other area. The idea of infinity is an integral part of the big idea of equivalence.

Disciplinary knowledge

In many of the conversations around curriculum design which have been taking place recently, teachers and school leaders have been looking at how to address not only the substantive knowledge of subjects, but also the disciplinary knowledge. The substantive knowledge of a subject is the 'what' of a subject, i.e. what is the body of knowledge that comprises a subject? Disciplinary knowledge is the 'how' of a subject, i.e. how do experts within those subject domains go about finding or creating the substantive knowledge? What is interesting about some of the big ideas listed above is that they form part of mathematical disciplinary knowledge. For example, pattern spotting, proof, classification and comparison are all activities in which mathematicians engage themselves. By ensuring that we are aware of these big ideas when planning, we can provide opportunities for our pupils to engage in these activities too, allowing them to be mathematical and to behave mathematically.

Planning with big ideas

It's incredibly important to have a common understanding and common language around big ideas that all adults in your school are aware of. If teachers know what the key big ideas are and, crucially, how they are manifested across the maths curriculum, they will be able to develop pupils' understanding of the ideas as they teach, creating links across mathematical domains and giving pupils an understanding of the interconnectedness of the subject. This common language and understanding will then develop in your pupils, helping them to make sense of seemingly disparate concepts as they learn about them. This is why, for all instructional sequences, it's important to explicitly identify the big ideas that will come up as you teach. Doing this will encourage you to consider how to link this current learning with what pupils already know, helping them to build a coherent schema of interconnected mathematical knowledge. This is what will encourage our pupils to have a deeper understanding of what they are learning.

Identifying big ideas: key points

- Within the discipline of mathematics, there are a number of big ideas that crop up again and again across the different domains that make up the subject.

- There is no definitive list of big ideas, but different maths educators have attempted to identify the most important ones.

- Big ideas bind together seemingly separate concepts in maths and provide links across the maths curriculum. By ensuring that all teachers have an understanding of the role that big ideas play in maths, pupils will be supported to link new learning to what they already know.

- When planning an instructional sequence, it's important to identify the big ideas that will come up in your teaching and consider how to make links between this new learning and what your pupils have already learned.

8 Identifying prerequisites

Mathematics is a hierarchical subject in which knowledge is built incrementally upon previous knowledge, forging connections between concepts in the minds of our pupils. To know what we must teach our pupils next about a particular area of mathematics, we must find out what they already know. New learning should always be anchored to existing learning. As well as having an awareness of how we might make this anchoring effective, we need to appreciate that new learning is largely dependent on previous knowledge. Let's look at a concrete example from the Key Stage 2 curriculum to demonstrate this. Take a piece of paper and solve the following calculation using the standard long multiplication algorithm:

$$56 \times 27$$

Once you have done this, work through the calculation again, this time paying attention not to answering the question but to thinking about what knowledge (both declarative and procedural) you need to solve it. Make a list of what a pupil would need to know if you were going to teach them this method of calculation.

Here is my list:

- Multiplication table facts (to calculate the product of each individual multiplication).
- The distributive law (to know that the sum of 56×20 and 56×7 is equal to 56×27).
- That the result of multiplying 50 and 2 will be ten times larger than the result of multiplying 5 and 2.
- Column addition (to add the two products to find the final answer).

This is the most basic level of knowledge that a pupil needs before they could be taught to calculate 56×27 successfully. The point of this is that we shouldn't be teaching children this particular method of calculating if they don't have a secure understanding of the knowledge on which this method relies – that is, the prerequisite knowledge.

While the importance of identifying what pupils already know may seem self-evident to some degree, the reality is that this stage is frequently missed out of the planning process. In many schools, teachers are obliged to follow a pre-ordained scheme of work which is set in stone for each year group. It is thus the job of the Year 3 teachers to teach the Year 3 programme of study from beginning to end, regardless of whether their pupils are ready for it or not. This approach to teaching maths simply doesn't work, as we have seen. Pupils need to be taught the next bit of maths which will build on their previous knowledge, not what the curriculum dictates should be taught next. As discussed earlier, you should try to avoid simply identifying what has previously been taught. Instead you need to concern yourself with what has actually been learned. While you may have taught pupils the features of a number of polygons in the past, for example, it's important that you assess their current knowledge, checking that they have retained what they were taught before moving on.

Failing to take into account whether or not our learners have the prerequisite knowledge needed to be successful will have one of two consequences. It could be, and this is the most likely scenario, that pupils will simply be unable to access the new learning. Without an understanding that all pupils can be successful at learning maths, this sort of failure is often presumed to be a failure on the part of the pupils, and this can only reinforce the assumption that these pupils are not good at maths and are unable to learn it. While few teachers would say this explicitly, the implicit assumption may still be there.

The other possibility is that some pupils will be able to muddle through in the lessons and perform acceptably. However, as this performance is not built upon solid foundations, it's unlikely to lead to deep and sustainable learning over time. This will result in gaps in pupils' knowledge, and these gaps, whether large or small, have the potential to wreak havoc in later learning. Therefore, regardless of the age or year group of your pupils, a priority should be to identify and consider the prior knowledge needed to be successful and to build sustainable learning based on this.

This means that once the coherent learning steps of a sequence have been identified and ordered, it is necessary to identify the prerequisites for success in the initial learning step. This involves asking the question, 'What do my pupils need to know in order to access this learning?' This is not something that needs to be undertaken from scratch; many maths educators have carefully considered the order in which the maths curriculum should be taught. Some commercially available products will identify prerequisites or prior learning that is necessary to know before a new concept is taught, although I always find it helpful to augment this by working through example questions that pupils will have to tackle themselves as part of the instructional sequence (as we did above). Doing this very deliberately and constantly considering what pupils need to know in order to access the learning will allow you to identify all of the necessary prerequisites.

Once you have identified the prerequisites – the key knowledge that pupils will require to successfully access the first learning step of your instructional sequence – you should assess your pupils' proficiency in them. This assessment, which should happen before any teaching of the new instructional sequence has taken place, ensures you know where your pupils are in terms of their knowledge of the prerequisites. They may well have been taught them in the past, but have they *learned* them? Are they still confident in their use? This diagnostic assessment, delivered before any new teaching takes place, is a key element of teaching for mastery. It will ensure that you have the best possible idea of what your pupils already know, and this will allow you to identify the gaps in knowledge which must be filled before moving on to the new learning.

In these diagnostic assessments, you should be looking for a high success rate – remember, these assessments are testing knowledge that you expect pupils to have already, rather than what you're planning to teach them next. If the assessments show there are certain prerequisites that pupils are struggling with, then you must first teach these prerequisites. This may seem obvious, but it's incredible how infrequently this tends to happen. In effect, this gives you a mini instructional sequence for any of the prerequisite knowledge that your pupils need to know before proceeding with the rest of the unit.

Once pupils have demonstrated that they are secure with the prerequisites for the instructional sequence, you can move on to the first of the learning steps in the sequence. However, it's important to bear in mind that, as with all assessments, the scores that pupils achieve are reflective of their knowledge, but also reflect on the quality of the assessment. In the next chapter I will consider how you can design high-quality assessments which will match your needs and give you the information that you require.

Identifying prerequisites: key points

- For any new mathematical learning, there will be prerequisite knowledge that pupils need in order to be successful in their new learning.
- After identifying the learning steps for a new instructional sequence, it's essential to consider what the prerequisite knowledge consists of.
- This knowledge must be assessed before you begin teaching the new instructional sequence.
- Any prerequisites which are not firmly understood by pupils should be taught and assessed to ensure that pupils will be able to access the new learning in your instructional sequence.
- Once pupils are secure with the prerequisites, the learning of the new instructional sequence can begin.

9 Assessment

Assessment is a huge topic. Countless books, blogs, essays and dissertations have been written on the subject. In one short chapter I can't possibly cover all that needs to be said about assessment, but what I hope to do is to explain clearly its central role in teaching for mastery. In this chapter we will look at some different ways in which you can assess the learning of your pupils and how each approach relates to teaching for mastery.

You may well have noticed that this book talks about assessment a great deal. On the one hand, this is obvious – no one would dispute that assessment is intrinsic to the process of teaching and learning. However, it seems that we are in an era where assessment – especially more formal assessment such as testing – is frequently maligned. Of course, there is much, much more to assessment than just testing, but tests remain a crucial tool in any teacher's armoury. I hope that all readers will question the prevailing narrative in some circles that more testing is necessarily a bad thing. We will come back to this point later in the chapter.

The most common dichotomy in assessment is that of formative versus summative assessment. Broadly speaking, summative assessment refers to any assessment practices which seek to measure the performance of pupils at the end of a sequence of teaching (or several sequences of teaching) to see what has been learned. The key defining characteristic of summative assessment – when it is contrasted with formative assessment – is that it does not feed back into the teaching process. A GCSE or A level examination is a perfect example of a true summative assessment, as students take the tests after they have completed their programmes of study, and don't receive results or feedback until after they have finished that particular stage of schooling.

Formative assessments, on the other hand, are defined as assessment practices where the results feed back into the teaching process, allowing teachers to tailor future instruction in an effort to match it carefully to what pupils don't know or have misunderstood. As tests are often used summatively, the words 'testing' and 'summative assessment' are often used synonymously. However, if a test is used to inform future teaching, it is of course a formative assessment. In teaching for mastery, the vast majority of assessments, including tests, are used formatively. Tests at the end of an instructional sequence are used to identify areas that pupils have not yet been successful with. Based on this, additional teaching can be planned to remedy the situation.

Teachers assess all the time, and in my experience more effective teachers tend to assess more frequently than less effective teachers. Much of this assessment takes place in lessons, through oral questioning, written examples and activities designed for our pupils. This assessment is incredibly important as it feeds directly into how you are teaching in the moment. While there are many techniques to support you to do this better, I'm keen to focus on the more formal assessments that you can use to gauge your pupils' performance over multiple lessons and learning steps. Let's now look in turn at two different forms of assessment that are crucial elements in teaching for mastery: low-stakes quizzing and testing.

Low-stakes quizzing

Quizzing and testing are very similar on the surface. It could probably be argued that the only difference between the two is that they have different names, but I think there are three important differences to consider. Firstly, quizzes should be thought of as lower stakes than a test and will be used more regularly in lessons. Secondly, quizzes are generally shorter than tests and can be completed quickly as part of a lesson. Finally, the purpose of quizzes and tests are different: while tests are designed to see what our pupils know and are able to do, a quiz, while also performing this role, has an important additional purpose, which is to serve a useful role in facilitating something called retrieval practice.

Retrieval practice occurs when pupils are given the opportunity to recall something stored in their long-term memories. Imagine that you want someone to learn something. Which approach would be more effective?

- Approach A: teach them the material three times and then test them once.
- Approach B: teach them the material once and then test them three times.

The intuitive answer is that Approach A would be the most effective, or so I thought when this proposition was first put to me. However, as is the case with much intuition, it's incorrect. Having to recall previously learned content is more effective than being retaught it multiple times. Although the reasons for this are hard to discern, it has been hypothesised that the effort of having to recall something from long-term memory, rather than simply being told it again, helps to strengthen future attempts to recall it. Each time something is recalled from memory, the easier it becomes to retrieve in the future. This is why regular low-stakes quizzes are important. Their main purpose is to give pupils the opportunity to *recall* what they know, rather than it being an *assessment* of what they know; that is to say, it's more of a teaching tool than an assessment tool, and so the scores don't matter as much as they might do in a test. What matters is that pupils are being given the chance to recall what they have previously been taught. The more that pupils are given the chance to recall facts and procedures, the greater the ease with which they will be able to successfully retrieve them in future.

Quizzes should be short in length, quick to administer and comprised of questions that can be easily answered. A quiz or two per week isn't too onerous to implement, as they should usually be possible to complete in five minutes or less. Quizzing this often will ensure that pupils are given regular opportunities to recall what they know. And while I made the point above that scores don't matter too much here, they will still give you useful information as to how your pupils are getting on.

Most lessons will contain questions for pupils to answer, often as part of an activity (see Section 3 on activity design). The differences between an activity and a quiz are worth considering. Firstly, an activity usually assesses much of the new learning that has been taught in the current learning step, whereas a quiz typically tests knowledge from previous learning steps and instructional sequences. Secondly, an activity may have a broad variety of questions, including complex problems which take time to solve, whereas a quiz tends to have fewer questions that are quicker to solve. Thirdly, an activity may be scaffolded for some pupils to help them to grasp the new learning, and you may also be circulating around the class during an activity, supporting any pupils who need help to answer the questions.

Quizzes, on the other hand, should be completed independently to give a snapshot of what pupils are able to do without help.

In terms of quizzes being low stakes, it's important to bear in mind that, while the stakes of any assessment are partly intrinsic (SATs are high-stakes assessments for schools, whether we tell pupils this or not), the messages that we give to pupils also play a role in how they are perceived. This perception will come from both implicit and explicit messages that we give to pupils regarding quizzing. Explicitly, you should tell pupils that quizzing is a useful tool to help them remember and practise what they already know. You should tell them that the content of a quiz is based around what they already know and are able to do, so they should think hard and try to remember. You should also tell them that they will practise quiz questions again and again, giving them the opportunity to improve. Along with these explicit messages, by showing that you are concerned with improvement between quizzes rather than just the raw scores, and by making quizzes a regular and unremarkable part of your daily practice, you can demonstrate to pupils that they are low-stakes assessments.

Testing

More formal tests are also an integral part of teaching for mastery but before looking in detail at this, I want to briefly address the current discussions around tests and other formal assessments and the role they play in our education system today. Testing is often accused of contributing to anxiety in schools and pupils currently in school are frequently labelled as being 'the most tested generation'. While this may be true, testing and other formal assessments are a central part of the education system and should remain so. Of course tests can cause some stress, but this is not abnormal and if handled well there is no reason for them to cause undue pressure for pupils. Reminding pupils that they take tests to find out what they know and to practise their skills, and that doing this allows them to improve, can help to assuage any nerves that they may have about the tests. The majority of test anxiety comes from the messages that pupils are given by adults, so if adults, especially teachers, make it clear to children that tests are a normal part of education and that, while important, are not the sole measure of their performance, we can start to create a situation where tests are regarded as the norm.

This is necessary because tests are important. They give us information that we can't glean from other sources, including finding out what pupils can do independently, especially in situations where the method for answering a question is initially opaque. Seeing if pupils are able to use their mathematical knowledge to think through an unfamiliar problem independently is best assessed through a test, because if the same question was presented in a lesson, we'd likely help pupils who were stuck. Throughout this book I advocate for a great deal of assessment, including regular testing. The main reason for this is that it lets you know how pupils are progressing in their learning and allows you to assess what they can remember of previous learning (i.e. have they actually learned it?). However, a happy side effect of regular testing is that it allows pupils to become accustomed to the process. This normalises testing and will in the long term help to reduce pupil stress surrounding testing. The more often we are exposed to a stimulus, the more accustomed we become to it and the less it scares us.

When teaching for mastery, there are a number of points where I suggest testing should be used. At the beginning of an instructional sequence, it's important to test children's understanding of the sequence's prerequisites: the prior knowledge they must have to enable them to successfully access the new learning. You can't assume that pupils have retained this learning just because they've been taught it before, so it's important that you test it, giving you a clear picture of what your pupils know.

You should also test at the end of an instructional sequence, to ensure your pupils are ready to move on. Testing what you've taught in the sequence will help you to identify areas that may need additional teaching and practice before you can progress with your next instructional sequence. It should be said that pupils might perform well immediately after being taught something but seem to forget it later. This is normal, and why it is so important to continually review prior learning so that pupils have the chance to recall what they've learned previously. So bear in mind that, while testing at the end of a unit is important, success in the test is no guarantee that pupils have learned the content for the long term. This is the distinction between learning and performance that was mentioned earlier, and is something to be very aware of as a teacher.

It should also be noted that these prerequisite and end-of-sequence tests are assessing a particular mathematical domain. They are identifying pupils' knowledge within the narrow area of maths covered by the scope of your instructional sequence. As well as testing as part of your instructional sequences, you should also build in opportunities for pupils to demonstrate their cumulative knowledge over the course of a series of instructional sequences, as well as over the course of a year. These tests should assess across domains and instructional sequences, identifying what pupils have learned over a period of time. They are more akin to true summative assessments.

Such tests could happen perhaps at the end of a term, but you can of course still use the information gleaned from them to inform future teaching. The importance of these cross-domain tests, as opposed to start and end-sequence assessments, should not be understated. It will be these tests that start to measure learning as opposed to simply performance, as they will include questions from a variety of different domains which are presented in different forms. They will begin to truly test what pupils can do independently in a situation where they will be unaware of what mathematical domain or type of knowledge is being tested. The ability to do this successfully is what we want for all of our pupils.

A crucial point to bear in mind about these tests is that they must match the curriculum that has been taught. A child who scores 50 per cent on a test which is assessing things that haven't yet been learned in school is very different from a child who scores 50 per cent on a test perfectly matched to what has been taught, although the two scores are the same. Too often, when we buy 'off-the-shelf' assessments they simply don't match the taught curriculum. This limits their usefulness as a diagnostic tool. For an assessment to truly begin to tell us something, it must be testing what has been taught. Having said that, writing bespoke assessments is difficult, as well as being time-consuming. This leaves us with a dilemma about where we get our assessments from. Do we buy something pre-written and risk it not matching our curriculum or do we spend a lot of time and effort creating assessments which match our curriculum but risk being poorly constructed?

I believe there are two ways of getting around this problem. Firstly, some high-quality commercial programmes have sets of assessments that match the progression of their units and lessons. If schools choose to buy into such programmes, it's possible to use their assessments, safe in the knowledge that they will match the taught content. Alternatively, for schools who want to create assessments that match their own bespoke instructional sequences, treating bought-in tests as a question bank from which to draw is an effective approach, as it allows you to create something that matches your instructional sequences while mitigating the pitfalls of writing your own questions. An externally created set of questions is likely to be of higher quality than anything many teachers could produce themselves, but we can use our knowledge of our school's curriculum to create our own assessments from these questions. Additionally, by taking the time to read and become familiar with these questions, you'll begin to appreciate what makes a good question, helping you to develop your own examples to supplement the selection that you already have.

Assessment: key points

- While formative and summative assessment are frequently compared and contrasted, when teaching for mastery, all assessment is formative because the information gleaned from any assessments informs future teaching.
- Assessment can be thought of as being split into three types: in-lesson assessment, low-stakes quizzing and testing, all of which are integral to teaching for mastery.
  - In-lesson assessment comprises questions that we ask orally and activities that pupils have to complete during a lesson.
  - Low-stakes quizzing involves giving pupils regular, short quizzes which test current and previous learning. These quizzes can be repeated for retrieval practice, strengthening the ease with which pupils can recall what they have previously learned.
  - Testing involves more formal assessments, which may assess learning in a single mathematical domain or across several domains, depending on when it's used. Tests are used at the start and end of instructional sequences to identify what pupils already know and what they have learned.
- Tests should match the curriculum that they are assessing, but good tests are hard to design. Use existing high-quality test questions as a bank from which to draw, and use these questions to devise tests that will truly assess your taught curriculum.

10 Delivering an instructional sequence

Once you have designed your instructional sequence, it's time for you to deliver it to your pupils. There are a number of key stages in this process, which are identified and discussed here. But first, before getting into the stages of delivering an instructional sequence it's important to recap the distinction between lessons and learning steps.

Lessons versus learning steps

When thinking about an instructional sequence it's important to bear in mind that a lesson is the not the same as a learning step. The terms are not analogous and should not be considered so. A learning step is a small, coherent mathematical unit that can be taught to a group of pupils. We know that individual pupils learn at different rates and different groups of pupils will also learn at different rates. We can't foresee how quickly a class will grasp a particular mathematical idea, and there is no reason to think that learning will happen in neat lesson-sized chunks. However, we often behave as if that this is exactly what will happen.

A lesson is a unit of time; a learning step is a unit of mathematics. The two will rarely match up. A sequence of 15 learning steps could take 15 lessons to deliver, but it could equally well take five lessons or 25 lessons. While planning your learning steps, you should be aware that each step is unlikely to fit into the neatly timetabled unit of 'one lesson'. There is no reason why the learning in a particular step should always fit into a certain arbitrary parcel of time, and it would be a mistake to expect it to happen like this.

Therefore, when teaching each learning step, you should bear in mind that it may well cross the boundaries of lessons. Of course you will still plan in terms of lessons, as they're the organisational units into which a school day is divided, but you should always keep the learning steps firmly in mind. An almost irresistible urge that you must try to avoid is to start each lesson with something new. If you are partway through teaching a learning step, but your pupils didn't quite finish the activity on which they were working, you must pick it up in the next lesson at the point where you left off. Otherwise, your pupils would miss out a chunk of their learning. If you were reading your class a book – presuming that you wanted them to follow the narrative – and you ran out of time partway through a chapter, you wouldn't start reading again at the start of the next chapter the next day. Lessons are not always neat chunks of learning, and we should not expect them to be, so don't miss out or rush over crucial bits of learning just because the clock has run down.

The stages of delivering an instructional sequence

The following stages of delivering an instructional sequence are all essential when teaching for mastery. They rely on each other and together they'll ensure that pupils have the best chance of learning each step within the sequence. Let's now look at each of the stages in turn, considering their importance to the overall scenario of teaching an instructional sequence.

Assess the prerequisites

The purpose of identifying prerequisites before beginning to teach an instructional sequence is to ensure that pupils have the necessary knowledge to access the new learning. If they don't, the new learning is likely to fail. This assessment can take the form of a test. If there are prerequisites that pupils are not confident with, these must be taught before proceeding with the new learning of the instructional sequence.

As you'll be working with a whole class, it is of course likely that different pupils will have different knowledge of the prerequisites. Some pupils will be ready to progress with the new learning and others will not. If there are pupils in your class who need to work on any of the prerequisites, you will need to teach these first to ensure that everyone is able to progress to the new learning.

Teach any necessary prerequisites

Once you have assessed the prerequisites that some pupils are not secure with, you must teach them as learning steps in their own right. For the pupils who are already secure with the prerequisites, this will mean some over-learning and practising what they already know. This is not a bad thing; in fact, it's incredibly important. Too often, we push pupils on to new learning after demonstrating competence just once, and we don't give them a chance to consolidate what they know. At the same time, it's important that pupils are encouraged to deepen their understanding once they are confident with the basics. Designing effective activities (see Section 3 on activity design) will ensure that pupils who have already grasped the prerequisites are given the opportunity to deepen their understanding of the content too.

Teach the learning steps

Once all pupils are secure with the prerequisites, it's time to progress with the learning steps of the instructional sequence. The steps should progress in the order planned, with carefully designed activities to allow opportunities for practice, which will develop your pupils' ability to be mathematically fluent, to reason mathematically and to solve problems. The activities should be designed to allow pupils to deepen their understanding of concepts and procedures. As discussed above, learning steps will frequently span lessons, and this is not a problem.

Throughout this teaching phase, it's essential to assess continually to see how pupils are progressing in their learning. Their performance in activities that are set in lessons will give an indication of this, but low-stakes quizzes will also feed into the picture. Low-stakes quizzes are helpful because, by having a range of questions that have been taught in different lessons, they require harder thought than a series of questions all of a similar sort.

Intervene for pupils who need support

As the instructional sequence progresses, it's important to support the pupils who may need additional time or help in order to grasp the learning. In class, that might require scaffolding an activity to allow pupils to access the learning more easily. Out of class, it might require additional teaching time in a smaller intervention group. The coming chapters on intervention and scaffolding will describe how this could be organised.

Assess the unit

Once the instructional sequence has come to an end, it's important to assess your pupils' learning. Assessment will, of course, have been taking place throughout the sequence. However, a test at the end of the unit will assess your pupils' ability to recall what they've learned throughout the sequence and if they are able to apply what they've learned to unfamiliar questions and scenarios. The results of this assessment will inform you whether or not your pupils are ready to proceed on to another instructional sequence, or if they need additional teaching.

Reteach any steps not understood

To ensure as firm a foundation as possible, pupils should have demonstrated success with each learning step in the sequence. If the end-of-sequence test shows there are steps which pupils are unsure of, these steps will need to be retaught. As with the prerequisites, astute activity design can ensure that pupils who have grasped the learning are given the opportunity to practise and deepen their understanding while others grasp the key learning of the step.

Following these steps will ensure that all pupils have the best possible chance of accessing the new learning of a sequence, and will help to build learning that is deep and durable. The next section of this book will look in more detail at how you can design and structure each individual learning step.

Delivering an instructional sequence: key points

The following list reflects the stages of delivering an instructional sequence. The structure should be familiar – a cycle of assessing and teaching, assessing and teaching. This cycle is the essence of teaching for mastery.

- Assess the prerequisites.
- Teach any necessary prerequisites.
- Teach the learning steps.
- Intervene for pupils who need support.
- Assess the unit.
- Reteach any steps not understood.

Section 2 Learning step design and delivery

Once you've designed your instructional sequence, it's time to start designing and teaching individual learning steps. These first steps may be prerequisites that certain pupils are lacking proficiency in, or they may be the initial learning steps of the unit. Either way, the process is the same. There is no magic formula for the perfect maths learning step. Any kind of checklist of elements to include will fail to cover the full gamut of what can happen when you teach maths and no planning proforma can capture every scenario. For this reason, please don't think the following chapters are elements that should be 'ticked off' when designing learning steps. Rather, think of them as a toolkit from which you should draw, depending on factors such as the mathematical content you're teaching, the pupils you're teaching, and the point in the instructional sequence at which you happen to be. While some of the following elements should become an intrinsic part of the vast majority of your lessons (review, for example) others will not always be appropriate.

The following chapters will cover the importance of reviewing prior learning, to bind learning steps together coherently, and the importance of teaching with variation to ensure pupils gain a full understanding of the concepts and procedures that we're teaching them. I will look at how language can be used to develop pupils' learning, and how interventions can support those pupils who need it. The final chapter in Section 2, 'Delivering a Learning Step', will look at how you can pull this all together.

11 Review

Review of prior learning is an absolutely essential element of any instructional sequence and should form an important part of any learning step. There are a number of reasons for this. Firstly, including an element of review during the teaching of each learning step links together a series of separate steps into one coherent whole. Rather than seeing each step or lesson as being distinct from the rest, review of what pupils last learned allows them to see that the learning steps are linked and relate directly to one another (see Figure 10). It helps us, as well as our pupils, to see the overarching thread that should run through each instructional sequence. Review is particularly important when a learning step spans multiple lessons, which is a common occurrence. Providing an overview of what pupils have previously been taught allows the transition from one lesson to another to be more seamless, enabling us to pick up where we left off more easily.

Secondly, review of previous learning also has the effect of activating pupils' prior knowledge. Psychologists theorise that knowledge is stored in the long-term memory in schemata. A schema is a collection of interrelated pieces of knowledge about a given topic or concept which expresses the relationships between linked ideas. For example, in your schema for 'New York City', you may have linked ideas such as 'pizza', 'Times Square', *The Godfather*, '9/11', 'Central Park' and so on. It's possible to 'activate' a person's schema by getting them to recall what they know about a particular idea. This brings to mind the idea itself as well as other knowledge relating to that idea. It's quite likely that you're now thinking about New York, perhaps remembering a holiday there, thinking about an episode of *Friends* or humming your favourite song by the Ramones. Everyone's schemata are different, but there will be common themes in most peoples' schema of any given idea.

In the classroom, if we activate our pupils' schema of prior learning by recalling what we've taught them previously, this will hopefully maximise the chance of them integrating new learning into their existing schemata, rather than remembering it as something in isolation. By making explicit links between learning steps, ideas and concepts, you can help pupils to build up coherent schemata of the mathematical concepts that you're teaching.

Finally, review is a crucial tool for teachers to use because of the impact that both forgetting and remembering have on long-term memory. As outlined in the glossary, 'learning' can be defined as a change in long-term memory. Therefore, for pupils to have learned, they must be able to remember what we've taught them; if they cannot remember what we've taught them, they have not learned it and the content will need teaching again. While this might seem obvious, it's often the case that teachers do very little to explicitly encourage their pupils to remember what they've learned after they've been taught something. It was certainly not something that I explicitly focused on early in my teaching career, although I did often become frustrated when my pupils forgot what they had previously learned.

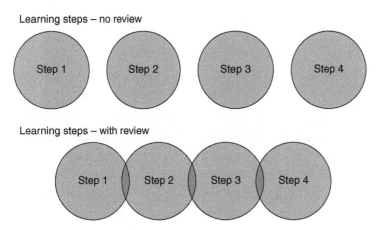

Learning steps – no review

Step 1   Step 2   Step 3   Step 4

Learning steps – with review

Step 1   Step 2   Step 3   Step 4

Figure 10

Peps Mccrea, author of *Memorable Teaching*, emphasises that as teachers, we must start with the assumption that our students will forget what they have learned *unless we take deliberate steps to help them remember.*'[14] Thankfully, review is an excellent way of helping your pupils to build durable long-term memories so that what they learn is not forgotten forever. However, as contradictory as it seems, forgetting does have an important role in remembering. We know this to be true thanks to the work of a German psychologist in the late nineteenth century who was fascinated by what we remember and how we forget.

Ebbinghaus and his curves

Hermann Ebbinghaus (1850–1909) is now best known for his work on human memory and the impact that forgetting has on remembering. He tried to remember sets of nonsensical syllables and attempted to recall them at various intervals, recording his successes and failures along the way. He plotted this information graphically, and the results of this are his well-known 'forgetting curves' (see Figure 11).

These curves show that, after learning something just once, forgetting happens at a fairly rapid rate, and the chance of the information being remembered over time is typically very small. However, each time the information is reviewed, the rate of forgetting afterwards is slower (the curve becomes shallower) and the chance of the information being remembered is higher (the curve starts to level off at a higher percentage). Each additional reminder after a period of forgetting continues to increase the proportion of what has been learned. Repeating something several times ensures that newly learned information is eventually retained to a very high degree. Ebbinghaus' findings have been replicated more recently[15] and now there are a variety of websites and apps which all make use of the idea of spaced reminders to help users to learn new information.

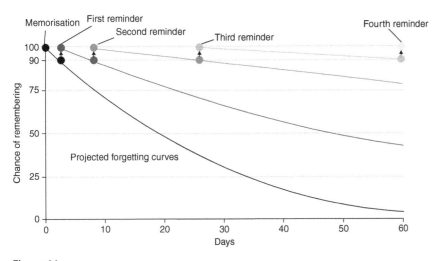

Figure 11

The rate at which information is forgotten depends upon a number of factors, including the nature and complexity of the information, how the information relates to the learner's existing knowledge, as well as other environmental factors. However, the pattern of forgetting is the same regardless of the speed at which it occurs – a large amount of information is quickly forgotten if it is not subsequently reviewed or recalled. Attempting to remember something after a single exposure is unlikely to result in a high level of retention; regular repetition over a longer period of time is necessary for this to take place. Hence the importance of regular review when we teach.

It's important that we build in time in all of our instructional sequences for review. This review should cover both recently learned information as well as that which has been learned in the past. The aim is to create a regular review of previously learned material to ensure that pupils are constantly having to remember what they've previously learned. Each time that this recall takes place for pupils, they will forget more slowly and recall more readily in the future.

Proximal and distal review

We've now identified two linked (but distinct) types of review, which I shall call proximal review and distal review.

- **Proximal review:** review of the most recently covered learning. The purpose of this is to link together separate lessons and learning steps, and to activate pupils' schemata to effectively tether new content to what has already been learned.

- **Distal review:** review of content from earlier in the instructional sequence or from previous instructional sequences. The purpose of this is to encourage pupils to remember content that may have been partially forgotten in order to strengthen future recall.

Review

The idea of these two types of review is not new; for instance, it is referenced in Barak Rosenshine's excellent *Principles of Instruction* where he describes the purpose and importance of both 'daily review' and 'weekly and monthly review'.[16] These two types of review are interlinked and both important. It is vital to make time for both kinds of review to take place. In my experience, proximal review often happens in many classrooms, but distal review tends to be rarer.

It's essential that both proximal and distal review are regularly included in the learning sequence because the process of recalling and reviewing previous learning is what transforms knowledge from being something transitory, which is heard once but then forgotten, to being something that is durably embedded in the long-term memories of learners. Both the proximal and distal review portions of a lesson can take multiple forms, as there are a number of ways of reviewing prior learning effectively.

Proximal review could include a short oral recap or element of teacher explanation, perhaps paired with a modelled example or visual representation that has been used previously. It could include pupils practising a previously learned procedure or solving a mathematical problem. It could include a question which encourages pupils to reason about an aspect of the maths and articulate a clear answer. All of these activities should be presented in a similar way to what pupils are used to in lessons. The goal here is not to teach pupils something new, but to remind them of what they already know.

For distal review, a variety of questions of increasing difficulty about a particular concept may be appropriate, as well as problems that require pupils to draw on knowledge from different areas of maths. This is because distal review generally focuses on completed instructional sequences, so it's helpful to draw on a variety of material covered in different parts of the sequences.

Deciding how much time to spend on review is difficult and there's no single answer which will always be appropriate. However, it's important to bear in mind that review must not be seen as an optional extra, but as an integral part of the learning process for your pupils. All content will be new learning at one point or another, but without repetition through regular review, it's unlikely that the content will be successfully retained. Therefore, review is just as important as the new learning in any lesson. I think there is a natural tendency to regard new learning as more important and therefore to minimise the amount of time that is given over to review. I would argue that this is a mistake, as the new learning that we're trying to give precedence to in our lessons will be forgotten if we don't create time to review it in the future. Therefore, new learning and review rely on each other, with neither being successful without the other. Indeed, the longer that I teach, the more important I understand review to be, and consequently the more learning time I give over to review in my own teaching.

Case study: quadrants at Angel Oak Academy

At Angel Oak, where I led maths for five years, we developed a number of ways of including review in our maths lessons. One way that we found to be particularly useful for distal review was the use of quadrants (see Figure 12).

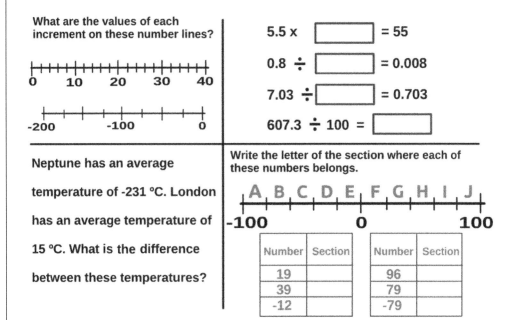

Figure 12

The Year 5 team at the time had introduced quadrants as a 'do now' activity for pupils entering the classroom at the beginning of maths lessons. The screen was split into four, with each quadrant containing a different activity. This would include things that had been learned previously, as well as mathematical staples such as multiplication and division facts to be recalled. As with all good 'do now' activities, these were designed to be questions that the pupils could complete with minimal support. Pupils would choose two of the four quadrants, complete them individually, and then the teachers would go through the answers to all four quadrants before beginning the new learning.

Over time, we developed this idea and formalised it somewhat. First, we decided that each quadrant would review a specific piece of prior learning, with each one focusing on practising a procedure or revisiting a concept from a different number of weeks ago: a learning step from one week ago, one from two weeks ago, one from four weeks ago and one from eight weeks ago (see Figure 13).

This meant that any new learning would be repeatedly reviewed at the start of a lesson, as an absolute minimum, at an interval one week, two weeks, four weeks and eight weeks. We also decided that each pupil should complete all four quadrants, rather than choosing two to answer. This ensured that every pupil would have to recall the content from every quadrant, rather than leaving out quadrants that they found more difficult. This change did mean that the proportion of each lesson given over to quadrants increased slightly, but we felt that this time was essential to ensure that children were given sufficient opportunity to recall and practise their prior learning.

Three years on from its introduction, we found this constant cycling of content by using quadrants to be hugely beneficial to our pupils' retention, as it means they are constantly revisiting previous learning and having the opportunity to practise. Quadrants are now used throughout the school as a way to start lessons. As well as using them in mathematics, the teachers have also started to use them in other subjects too, where they have proved to be just as effective.

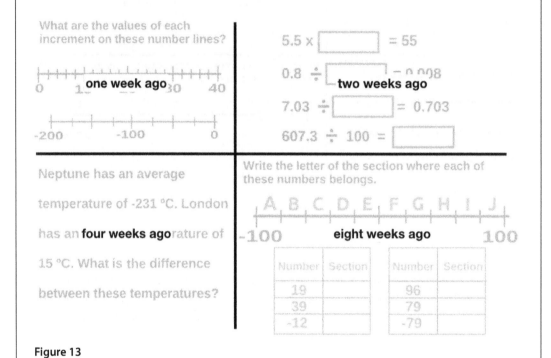

Figure 13

Review: key points

- Reviewing previously taught material is central to developing links between learning steps and to building durable learning.

- There are two key types of review: proximal and distal.

- Proximal review (reviewing the most recent learning step) ensures that each learning step links to what came before, creating a richly linked narrative of learning steps.

- Distal review (reviewing prior learning from further back) ensures that previously learned material is recalled, practised and integrated into the long-term memory.

- Review of previously learned information is just as important as covering new material. This part of each lesson/learning step should be prioritised, not minimised.

12 Conceptual variation

Variation theory, and its application in the classroom, is probably the most interesting and useful educational theory that I've learned about since becoming a teacher. Entire texts have been written on variation and its importance in teaching. I won't be going into this level of detail, but what I hope to do instead is to give you enough information to pique your interest, so you can consider how to use variation in your own teaching and then go on to find out more about the topic if you're interested.

In essence, variation theory suggests that we can learn a great deal by considering similarities, differences and change. A number of educators have studied variation and its applications in the classroom, and there are a range of terms and distinctions within this field. I will subdivide variation into 'conceptual variation' and 'procedural variation' as this is the distinction that I was first made aware of, and the one that I still consider to be the most useful in my maths teaching. Simply stated, conceptual variation deals with how we can teach static mathematical concepts through varying multiple representations, while procedural variation deals with how changing terms in equations affects other terms. I'll cover conceptual variation in this chapter and procedural variation in the next.

What is conceptual variation?

Conceptual variation deals with the idea that in order to fully know or understand something, you have to understand it from all angles. For example, consider yourself – you have a particular view of yourself, a unique perspective on who you are. However, everyone else who knows you sees you in a different light. You may be a child to your parents, but also a parent to your children. You may be a spouse or a sibling, an employee or an employer, a friend or an enemy, a neighbour, a landlord or tenant. To each other person, you are something quite different, and appreciating these different perspectives gives you a deeper understanding of who you are.

In maths, you teach your children any number of different concepts and ideas. When teaching these concepts, it's vital that you give your pupils the fullest possible understanding of them. For example, consider shape 'a' below:

If you ask your pupils what shape it is, I'm sure many would say that it's a diamond. Show the same pupils shape 'b', and the majority would be happy to say that it's a square. However, obviously they are both squares – shape 'a' is simply shape 'b' rotated by 45º. It's nice to show pupils shape 'c' to ask whether it is a diamond or a square, or to rotate a square slowly and ask at what point it becomes a diamond, before pointing out that all three are squares, regardless of orientation.

The reason for this misconception is insufficient conceptual variation in the teaching of squares. Pupils have not been shown enough (or any) examples of squares that are not prototypical; that is, squares that are not orientated so their sides are aligned horizontally and vertically. Pupils must understand that a square can be orientated any way, as orientation is a non-essential feature of a square. The essential

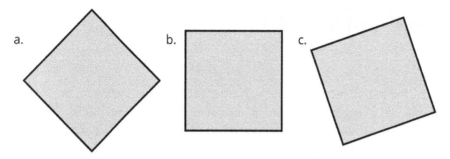

Figure 14

features are four right angles and four equal sides, but it can be orientated in any way, rotated through 360° and still be a square.

Pupils can only fully understand a mathematical concept and its boundaries through conceptual variation, whereby we vary the non-essential features of a concept to highlight its essential features. We change what we can and leave what we cannot. Through the careful variation of non-essential features, pupils build up a deeper understanding of a particular concept. It's helpful to look at concrete examples of this. Let's start with a non-mathematical analogy to give you the basic idea.

Is it a bird?

Imagine, if you can, a child who has never seen or heard of a bird. This child knows nothing about birds, and you want to teach her what a bird is. To start off with, you could show her a starling. Does this child now know what a bird is? No. She has seen one example of a bird, but not enough to have developed a deep knowledge of the concept of 'bird'. Next, you could show the child a bat. It's possible, even probable, that she would think the bat is a bird. Why? Well, the two animals share a number of similar features. They are both a similar size, they both eat insects, they both have wings, they are a similar colour and they can both fly. Unfortunately for our child, she doesn't know that none of these features are essential to being a bird. The essential features of birds are:

- Endothermic (warm-blooded)
- Feathered bodies
- Laying of hard-shelled eggs
- Toothless, beaked jaw
- Four-chambered heart
- Lightweight skeleton

Every bird shares these essential features. Anything that has all of these features is a bird; anything that lacks even a single one of these features is not. Therefore, despite a bat's four-chambered heart and lightweight skeleton, it is not a bird. So how can we ensure that children learn what a bird is, and what it isn't? The answer is through variation. For a child to understand what a bird is, they must be taught the essential features that all birds share and then be shown examples of birds with the non-essential features varied.

The best way to do this is to identify the non-essential features of the concept and then vary them one at a time through the examples that we expose our pupils to. Here are some of the non-essential features of a bird (i.e. the features that don't contribute towards whether something is a bird or not):

- Size
- Diet
- Ability to fly
- Colour
- Habitat

So firstly, we could show children birds of various sizes, from the ostrich to the hummingbird and everything in between. While the size has changed, the essential features (feathers, laying hard-shelled eggs, etc.) are still fulfilled. They are all birds. Next, we could vary the diet of the birds. From eagle owls, which can kill and eat calves, to ospreys that eat fish, to finches and swallows that mainly feed on seeds and insects respectively. Again, the diet doesn't matter because it's a non-essential feature. However, the essential features have remained the same. They are all birds.

And so on. This process could be repeated with as many non-essential features as possible, varying what can be varied to draw attention to what cannot – the essential features. Another important element of conceptual variation is teaching the non-concept: teaching what a concept is not, as well as teaching what it is.

Teaching the non-concept

The process that we've been through so far would start to give children a good understanding of birds. By including a range of standard and non-standard examples of birds, we've broadened their understanding of what a bird is. However, to have a secure understanding, children also need to know what a bird is *not*. It's this understanding that will help them to identify where the border lies between 'bird' and 'not a bird'.

> *'He cannot England know, who knows England only.'*

This aphorism, quoted by Ference Marton in his foreword to Mun Ling Lo's book *Variation Theory and the Improvement of Teaching and Learning*,[17] explains the idea of 'non-concept' nicely – we cannot understand what something is until we have considered what it isn't. It's only by comparing one thing to something else that we can truly understand what it is. For this reason, exposing learners to the non-concept is just as important as teaching the concept. In our bird example, the bat would be one example of demonstrating the non-concept, as it is similar to but not a bird. Let's explore this idea a little further by switching animals and considering elephants.

Imagine that we wanted to teach our child (who now has a firm understanding of what a bird is) about the concept of elephants. We would first teach them the essential features of elephants and then vary the non-essential features. Then we would come to teach them the non-concept, that is, what an elephant is not. This sounds simple at first; after all there are an incredibly large number of things that are not elephants. When pressed to identify something that is not an elephant, many people would choose a mouse, perhaps for the association that we tend to have between the two animals.

On the face of it, the mouse is an obvious choice for not being an elephant: it's small where the elephant is large, soft where the elephant is rough, nimble where the elephant is lumbering. There is a world of difference between a mouse and an elephant. However, this world of difference is not helpful to us; we want to discover where 'elephant' stops and 'not-an-elephant' begins. If we can discern this, then we have a secure understanding of the concept of 'elephant'. Therefore, in searching for the non-concept of an elephant, a much more useful choice than a mouse would be a rhinoceros. Both animals are large, rough and lumbering. They have a great deal of similarities, but in the slight differences between the two animals is the border between them – the place where 'elephant' stops and 'not an elephant' begins. If we can identify a rhinoceros as not-an-elephant, we understand the concept of an elephant far better than someone who can only identify a mouse as not-an-elephant. Now, on to some mathematical examples.

Conceptual variation with triangles

Let's now look at how you could teach the concept of triangles through conceptual variation. First, you must decide on the essential features of a triangle and state them as simply as possible. For example:

A triangle is a polygon with exactly three sides and three vertices.

That is the simplest definition of a triangle that I can devise, as the fact that it is two-dimensional and has straight sides is included within the definition of a polygon. Shapes that meet the criteria in this definition are triangles, while anything that does not can't be a triangle. Now consider the non-essential features of triangles that I can vary to draw attention to the essential features of 'polygonal', 'three sides' and 'three vertices'.

I could vary:

- Size
- Orientation
- Angle sizes/side length
- Colour

None of these features make something a triangle or not, and so by varying them one by one, we can demonstrate to our pupils what makes a triangle a triangle (see Figure 15). This means that when they encounter triangles that aren't prototypical, they can see past the non-essential features and recognise that a polygon with three sides and vertices is always a triangle.

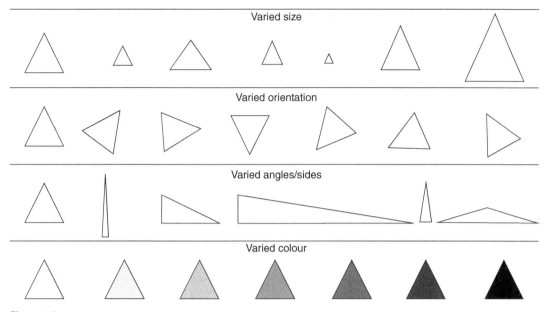

Figure 15

In terms of non-examples of a triangle, I would probably use a delta, curve one side, and slightly change one vertex (see Figure 16). These examples all have something of a triangle about them, but if pupils have been taught with conceptual variation, they should be able to easily discern that none of the three are triangles.

Figure 16

Teaching with conceptual variation gives the best possible chance of our pupils understanding a concept to its fullest extent – the goal for all the pupils that we teach.

Conceptual variation: key points

- There are two key types of variation – conceptual variation and procedural variation.

- Conceptual variation involves how we present particular concepts to pupils. We must vary the non-essential features of a concept to highlight its essential features. This gives pupils a deep understanding of the concept.

- As well as presenting multiple representations of a concept, we must also present pupils with examples of the non-concept, i.e. what the concept is not.

- Non-examples should be as close to the concept as possible whilst not actually being the concept – what is almost the concept but not quite. This allows pupils to discern the borders of a concept more clearly.

13 Procedural variation

Now that we have an understanding of the importance of conceptual variation, let's consider how procedural variation can be used in our teaching. Procedural variation involves varying the examples and questions we present to pupils in order to encourage them to notice things about the relationships between the numbers involved. By seeing how varying one term in an equation affects the other terms, we can start to see how the terms are linked. Procedural variation encourages us to use sets of questions in such a way that they become about more than just pupils finding the answer to a question and practising a procedure – they encourage an examination of the underlying structures at play.

   In the same way that when we teach pupils about fair tests in science we explain the importance of changing only one variable, when we teach using procedural variation we manage carefully what we change and what we keep the same. For example, let's say that we want our pupils to practise addition that bridges ten. We could give them a set of calculations like this in order to practise this procedure:

$$56 + 7 = \qquad 38 + 4 =$$

$$25 + 9 = \qquad 64 + 7 =$$

$$17 + 8 = \qquad 45 + 6 =$$

Our pupils could go through and answer these questions, which would probably be useful practice of what they have been learning about. However, these particular examples don't particularly allow us to make any further teaching points. Now consider the following set of calculations:

$$15 + 6 = \qquad 15 + 6 =$$

$$25 + 6 = \qquad 15 + 16 =$$

$$35 + 6 = \qquad 15 + 26 =$$

We could simply ask our pupils to answer these questions, which would allow them to practise addition that involves bridging ten in the way that the previous set of questions did. Some pupils might even notice, after having answered all the questions, that some answers are the same.

$$15 + 6 = 21 \qquad 15 + 6 = 21$$

$$25 + 6 = 31 \qquad 15 + 16 = 31$$

$$35 + 6 = 41 \qquad 15 + 26 = 41$$

We could also explicitly draw attention to what has happened in these sets of questions in order to make a teaching point about addition and how it works. In both sets above, we've started with the same calculation. In the first column we've then added ten to the first addend (going from 15 to 25). We can see that our sum has also increased by ten. This is also true for the next calculation (35 + 6). Again, we've added ten to our first addend and our sum has increased by ten. The questions in the second column show that the same pattern holds if we add ten to the second addend while keeping the first addend constant. We could then give pupils more examples of questions that make this same teaching point, and eventually we'll be able to give our pupils a generalised statement: *increasing an addend by the amount 'x' will increase the sum by the same amount.* We could give pupils a further set of questions where we increase both addends by a set amount:

$$15 + 6 = 21$$

$$25 + 16 = 41$$

$$35 + 26 = 61$$

$$45 + 36 = 81$$

In these examples, we've increased both addends by 10, and we can see that the sum has increased by 20, demonstrating that any changes to addends in addition are aggregated in the sum.

The questions, therefore, have a dual purpose: to allow pupils to practise a procedure, and to draw attention to key learning points about this procedure. Linking these learning points and observing how the same action can have different effects on different operations can also be a rich area of learning. For instance, look at the following set of subtraction calculations:

$$21 - 7 =$$

$$31 - 7 =$$

$$41 - 7 =$$

Once our pupils have had a chance to solve these questions, they will notice a similarity to the addition calculation above:

$$21 - 7 = 14$$

$$31 - 7 = 24$$

$$41 - 7 = 34$$

When the minuend is increased by an amount and the subtrahend remains the same, the difference increases by this amount too. However, a second set of calculations can introduce an interesting point which may at first confound pupils:

$$51 - 17 =$$

$$51 - 27 =$$

$$51 - 37 =$$

$$51 - 47 =$$

Once pupils have answered this set of questions, they may spot a pattern they didn't expect and which can even seem counter-intuitive when you first come across it. In the last three sets of questions, increasing one of the terms of a calculation resulted in the answer increasing in kind. However, this has not happened here:

$$51 - 17 = 34$$

$$51 - 27 = 24$$

$$51 - 37 = 14$$

$$51 - 47 = 4$$

In this case, increasing the subtrahend has caused the difference to decrease by the same amount. This realisation can help pupils to understand how addition and subtraction relate to each other, developing their understanding of both concepts.

We can use procedural variation in many areas of maths. For instance, when working on multiplication or division we can choose examples which show that doubling one factor in multiplication causes the product to double, doubling the dividend causes the quotient to double, but doubling the divisor causes the quotient to halve. An example of procedural variation in the domain of statistics could look like this:

Find the mean of the following sets of numbers:

a.   5, 6, 7, 8, 9
b.   5, 6, 7, 8, 14
c.   5, 6, 7, 8, 19

The possibilities inherent in procedural variation are infinite because mathematics is infinite. For instance, there are an infinite number of addition calculations with pairs of numbers which sum to 19. However, by being deliberate and purposeful in our selection of examples, we can draw pupils' attention to any number of interesting and important conceptual facets of the mathematical content, and this will allow our pupils to develop their knowledge and understanding of a concept. In all our examples, it's important to initially keep something the same – this allows the cause of any change to be identified.

In our maths lessons, we want pupils to 'notice' patterns in our questions, but it's important to clarify that this doesn't necessarily happen without your input as a teacher. Designing our questions with an element of procedural variation is only half the battle, as there may well be pupils who work through a set of questions (even the most carefully selected and designed set of questions) and not notice a pattern that is right in front of them. For this reason I strongly advocate for explicitly drawing our pupils' attention to what we want them to notice, rather than hoping that all pupils will discover it for themselves.

This can be done after pupils have been given the opportunity to notice a pattern for themselves. It does not need to be done in a heavy-handed way, through simply describing the pattern and asking pupils to spot it; rather, through careful questioning, such as by asking 'What do you notice about the answers to these questions?', we encourage pupils to look at something that they may have missed initially. Asking supplementary questions, such as 'Why do you think this might have happened?' or 'Can you think of another example where this might be true?' can encourage pupils to consider more deeply and interrogate what they are seeing. My key point remains, however, that we must not simply create a pattern and then expect, or hope, that all pupils will notice it and then understand the concept more deeply because of it.

When planning sets of questions for your maths lessons, it's not always necessary to design them with procedural variation in mind. Sometimes pure practice is the focus of your lesson, and there's no need to make a particular teaching point with the practice. Indeed, sometimes pupils can 'spot the pattern' and start to mechanically answer the questions by following the pattern without thinking. This is why I always like to break the pattern every so often, either by starting a new string of calculations or by putting in an unexpected question that doesn't follow the pattern. For example, we could have the following calculation string:

$$3 + 6 = \underline{}$$

$$13 + 6 = \underline{}$$

$$23 + 6 = \underline{}$$

If I were just to continue this pattern, there is the risk that pupils would simply continue the pattern too for subsequent questions, simply writing 39, 49, 59 for the answers without really considering the questions. To stop this from happening I could include a question which breaks the pattern, forcing pupils to refocus on the questions. The questions that I could choose to break the pattern are varied; I've included three different examples below with a brief explanation of what the purpose of each would be.

$$230 + 60 = \underline{}$$

This first question changes the order of the magnitude of the numbers, now dealing with numbers which are ten times larger. This question (and an associated string of questions afterwards) would draw pupils' attention to the fact that if both addends are made ten times larger, the sum will also be ten times larger. A similar point could also be made by making the numbers orders of magnitude smaller (for example 0.23 + 0.06). The ability to derive new facts from known facts, as illustrated above, is an incredibly important skill in mathematics.

$$33 + 16 = \underline{}$$

This second question changes the pattern by adding ten to both addends, causing the sum to increase by 20. This break in the pattern draws attention to the fact that changes in the addends are aggregated in the sum. This new question still focuses on adding without bridging ten, but brings pupils' attention back to the process of answering the question, rather than simply trying to 'follow the pattern'.

$$\underline{} + 6 = 49$$

This third question moves the focus from addition to subtraction, and explores pupils' understanding of the inverse relationship between addition and subtraction. The example still stays within the '3 + 6 = 9' pattern in the ones place, but causes a change of direction and requires a different procedure to find the solution.

What all three questions have in common is intentionality – in each case, I have chosen the question with a particular teaching point in mind. They are not random; they are thoughtfully chosen. And this is the key to procedural variation: choose your examples carefully and purposefully. There is a place for pupils answering a number of mixed calculations in order to practise and automatise a procedure that has been learned. However, I would argue that this practice need not always take place in lessons – in fact, it's probably an excellent candidate for a homework activity. In lessons, when you ask your pupils to practise, choose the questions yourself, think about what you could change and what you could keep the same, and consider the teaching points that you can make through these choices.

Procedural variation: key points

- Procedural variation (sometimes known as intelligent practice) is the process of selecting example questions carefully in order to make a teaching point about a particular concept or procedure. This is done by varying some values and keeping others the same to expose the relationship between them. It's using children's practice to encourage them to notice something about the mathematical concept being taught.

- Examples typically keep something constant in a series of questions in order to see how change in one thing affects another. This is rather like controlling variables in an experiment in order to see how the independent variable affects the dependent variable.

- It's important to 'break the pattern' every so often to ensure that pupils are considering the questions and not just spotting a shortcut to get an answer.

- Procedural variation can be used for questions in any area of mathematics and can be used to make a variety of teaching points. It can be used just as successfully with problems as it can with calculations.

- It's important to draw pupils' attention to patterns and have them consider why things have changed in that way – don't expect them to notice and understand the pattern themselves.

- Don't feel the need for every single set of questions that you devise to have a pattern; sometimes pupils simply need to practise a procedure to become skilled at it. However, don't underestimate the power of making a teaching point through the examples that pupils work with in lessons.

14 Language, talk and articulation

The ability to articulate an idea or concept is, in itself, an essential part of your knowledge and understanding of that concept. Language is the stuff of thought and, consequently, it's very difficult to think about something for which you have no language. Mathematics is an academic discipline with its own language, definitions and conventions, and learning this disciplinary knowledge is the right of every pupil. Thus, as maths educators, it's our responsibility to teach our pupils the language required for them to think about and discuss the mathematical content that they are learning.

Mathematical vocabulary

In some primary schools there seems to be a bit of resistance, especially with the youngest pupils, to teach the correct vocabulary for things. This resistance strikes me as strange for two reasons. Firstly, there is nothing inherently difficult or scary about mathematical vocabulary. We fully expect pupils in Reception to learn words like 'construction', 'assembly' or 'Gruffalo'. Are these words any more difficult to learn than 'addend', 'sum' or 'calculation'? Clearly not. Giving pupils, especially the youngest pupils, the correct language for ideas and concepts is empowering and exciting, and children love being able to use the correct words for things.

Secondly, it also makes teachers' jobs easier in the long run. Failing to use the correct names for things when they are first introduced is needlessly delaying the point at which they will have to learn the correct name. If at some point in the future we want pupils to know the correct name for something, why wait? If we call an 'equation' a 'number sentence' or something similar, at some point in the future we will have to explain this to our pupils, which seems like a waste of time. Why not just give everything the correct name from the start?

I'm not going to provide a full glossary of mathematical terms in this book – there are a number of good websites which clearly define mathematical terms, and it's not the key purpose of this book. However, I've included below the names for the constituent parts of the four operations. I do this because they are simple to learn, rarely taught to teachers during training, and are incredibly useful.

Addition:

$$6 + 9 = 15$$

$$\text{addend} \quad + \quad \text{addend} \quad = \quad \text{sum}$$

Subtraction:

$$17 - 11 = 6$$

$$\text{minuend} \quad - \quad \text{subtrahend} \quad = \quad \text{difference}$$

Multiplication:

$$7 \times 8 = 56$$

$$\text{factor} \quad \times \quad \text{factor} \quad = \quad \text{product}$$

$$\text{(multiplicand)} \qquad \text{(multiplier)}$$

Division:

$$29 \div 7 = 4 \text{ r}1$$

$$\text{dividend} \quad \div \quad \text{divisor} \quad = \quad \text{quotient} \quad \text{r} \quad \text{remainder}$$

It is so much easier to talk about – and to think about – the relationships between numbers when we have proper terms to name them. How much easier to think about how the minuend and subtrahend must change relative to each other in order to keep a constant difference than it would be without those names, thinking only vaguely in terms of 'this number' or 'that number'. Having a clear moniker for something makes our thinking clearer and brighter, so our mathematical thinking is clarified by the knowledge and use of the correct terminology.

I would strongly advocate that schools develop a list of shared vocabulary to enable pupils to hear and use the same vocabulary throughout their primary school career. This minimises the need to reteach or reassign vocabulary with pupils who are new to your year group. For example, it's inefficient to call the process of rearranging numbers within column addition and subtraction as 'regrouping' in some year groups and 'carrying' and 'borrowing' in others. Far more efficient to have a single word that is used and understood universally within a school. You will save time and improve clarity with this approach.

Opportunities for talk and articulation

Talk is a key component of mathematical learning, and our pupils should be given the opportunity to talk and discuss ideas in maths lessons. Wanting to avoid a checklist approach to lesson planning as mentioned previously, I won't say that *every* maths lesson should include the opportunity to talk, but I would argue that opportunities to talk are likely to be a feature of many good maths lessons. Chapter 19 will also address talk in the context of mathematical reasoning, but I include below some of the ways in which talk can be used more generally in maths lessons.

As mentioned previously, having the correct vocabulary for mathematical elements allows them to be thought about and therefore talked about. Talk is linked closely to variation, as covered in the two preceding chapters. Defining a concept with reference to its essential features is a key part of conceptual variation, and being able to identify and articulate what has changed and what has stayed the same in procedural variation is similarly important. Accurate mathematical vocabulary is necessary for this.

In Chapter 5 on planning coherent learning steps, I touched upon the use of stem sentences to give pupils the chance to talk in lessons. These can be very useful when coupled with the use of variation.

For example, a stem sentence such as 'When the dividend is doubled, I must _____ the divisor to keep the quotient the same' gives pupils language to describe the relationship between a number of division calculations when using procedural variation. This is important because it is the start of pupils' ability to generalise. Generalising is a key part of mathematics, and the ability to move from 'this happened in this case' to 'this happens in all cases' is crucial. A stem sentence such as this is a useful scaffold to get pupils used to thinking about mathematics in these terms. The other huge benefit of stem sentences is that through carefully choosing them, we can make them a valuable way of getting our pupils to notice what we want them to notice.

In addition to using stem sentences, pupils should have regular opportunities in maths lessons to talk more freely about the maths they are learning. Talk is essential for pupils as it allows them to clarify their thinking and to discuss and debate their ideas with others. It's also important for teachers, both as a means of assessment and as an indicator of pupils' understanding of an idea. The degree to which a pupil is able to articulate their understanding of a concept is a good gauge for how well they understand the concept.

Pupil to teacher talk

A good way to ensure that there's ample opportunity for mathematical talk in your lessons is to provide a great deal of questioning. When asking pupils to answer questions, you should try to supplement their answers with further probing questions, such as 'Why?' or 'How do you know?'. Such questions can start to expose pupils' thinking, and a classroom where these questions are commonplace encourages explanatory talk. Other commonly used mathematical questions, such as 'What do you notice?', the slightly less broad 'What can you tell me about _____?' and 'What's the same and what's different?', develop the expectation that pupils will be expected to notice things and look for patterns in lessons. Asking the questions with regularity will therefore have the long-term effect of encouraging pupils to notice things, to consider similarities and differences and to look for patterns. Asking these questions and building habits around their use will make noticing and pattern-spotting second nature to pupils. Eventually, they will start to notice and spot patterns without our questions or reminders being necessary.

Pupil to pupil talk

Of course, talk in lessons is not always easy to manage, especially in primary classrooms. Many teachers worry that talk will not be purposeful, and that it will therefore become a distraction to the learning rather than an integral part of it. While this can be true at times, the answer is not to remove talk from maths lessons but rather to train our pupils to engage in purposeful pupil-to-pupil talk. I think this training should start early on in schooling, with our youngest pupils. Building in opportunities for talk with simple scripted exchanges is a useful way to begin pupils' training in mathematical talk, using fairly simple sentence stems of the kind discussed previously.

This approach of using sentence stems has several benefits. Firstly, it gives pupils most of the language that they will need. Building coherent and correct sentences is not always easy for younger pupils, so this scaffolding is very helpful. Secondly, it gets pupils used to speaking in full sentences – a useful skill in any subject! Thirdly, this way of working is helpful for you as a teacher: if every pupil is using the same sentence stems, it becomes far easier to identify and redirect any pupils who are not on task or who are not using the correct language.

This type of practice early in a pupil's mathematical education builds the habit of purposeful mathematical talk, and this habit can be built upon in subsequent years. As pupils get older and the habit becomes more ingrained, it's possible to make the talk element more open and less formulaic, allowing pupils to select appropriate vocabulary and structure their talk independently. This will happen over time with sufficient practice. If pupils need more support in their talk, it's always possible to bring back sentence stems or suggested vocabulary to help them to structure their thinking. However it's done, talk is an incredibly useful part of mathematical learning, and its importance should not be underestimated.

Language, talk and articulation: key points

- Language is an essential component of mathematics teaching, and the ability to articulate mathematical thinking is an essential component of being a mathematician.

- Teach your pupils the correct names for terms and ideas as soon as they are introduced, no matter their age. If pupils are old enough to learn a concept, they are old enough to learn its name.

- Having names for mathematical concepts makes thinking about them much easier.

- Encourage discourse between yourself and your pupils by asking questions such as 'How do you know?' and 'Why?' to build a culture of purposeful mathematical talk in your classrooms and to check their understanding.

- Ask questions that encourage mathematical thinking such as 'What do you notice?', 'What pattern do you see?' and 'What's the same and what's different?'. These questions will lead to mathematical talk, but also encourage pupils to start asking these questions of themselves in the future.

- Train pupils to talk to each other about their learning in maths lessons, using suggested vocabulary and sentence stems as a scaffold at first.

- Build in opportunities for pupils to talk to each other purposefully about mathematics, encouraging them to explain their thinking and to justify it to their peers.

15 Intervention

An essential part of teaching for mastery is the aim that all pupils will progress through their learning at a broadly similar pace, enabling them to learn the mathematics curriculum in its entirety. We should have high expectations of all our pupils and know that they're fully capable of accessing the mathematical ideas we're teaching. We also know, however, that pupils are different and learn at different rates. It therefore follows that some pupils will need additional instruction and extra time to be able to grasp the same mathematical concepts as their peers. While these two ideas may sound contradictory, it is through intervention that we can square this circle. While there are a number of ways that teachers can 'intervene' to support pupils, in this chapter I refer to intervention as any additional instructional activities that take place *outside* the normal time allocated for maths lessons. This effectively means extra teaching for those pupils that need it.

The idea that some pupils will need extra support, or that they may have to progress more slowly through their learning than their peers, is clearly not surprising in itself. However, the fact that some pupils will need to go more slowly than their peers in the same amount of lesson time leads us to a depressing, if obvious, conclusion: these pupils are at risk of falling behind and never catching up. You can't catch up to someone who is faster than you by working more slowly than them. We cannot allow these pupils to fall behind, stay behind and then leave our primary schools without a solid mathematical foundation on which to build in the future. Therefore, we must give pupils who have fallen behind, or those who are in danger of falling behind, what they need – more teaching time. This is the only way to ensure that these pupils can become successful mathematicians.

This additional instruction falls into two broad categories of intervention. Firstly, there are 'keep-up' interventions, which aim to support those pupils who have not grasped a particular bit of learning and who may be in danger of falling behind their peers. Secondly, there are 'catch-up' interventions, aimed at those pupils who have gaps in their mathematical learning which are holding them back, meaning that they have already fallen behind. We shall look at both types of intervention to see how they can be used to support pupils.

Keep-up interventions

These interventions have one key goal: ensuring that all pupils are ready to move on to the next lesson or learning step together. As we want all our pupils to move together and to all be able to access the content, it's important that pupils don't get 'left behind' in the journey through an instructional sequence. Due to the differences between pupils, it's common that some will need a little additional support or time to grasp the learning in a particular learning step. This is precisely what a keep-up intervention seeks to do. It involves identifying the pupils who require some additional intervention, then devising appropriate support that can be delivered in an additional session after the lesson. These interventions are for those pupils who just need a push over the parapet to be ready for the next day's learning.

It's important to try to identify which pupils are not quite grasping the learning *during* a lesson, because if you can intervene and support them in the lesson then you may not need to provide additional support afterwards. The ideal scenario is that every pupil grasps the learning in a lesson and that no one requires additional intervention. This is made more achievable through paying close attention to how pupils are getting on during a lesson, rather than after it. For a long time, teachers have been in the habit of marking work after a lesson as a means of identifying how pupils have done. In the early years of my career, I would often work almost exclusively with one group of pupils per lesson, being unaware of how the majority of my class had got on until I sat down to mark their work at the end of the day. This approach was disastrous because it meant, in some cases, a whole lesson going by with a misconception or lack of understanding being allowed to fester.

Now my approach is to see each pupil during the lesson, often more than once, to ensure I can identify and address as many problems in the moment as possible. Techniques suggested by Doug Lemov in *Teach Like a Champion 2.0*, such as using a tracker – a document with the correct answers for easy reference and space to record common errors and the names of pupils who are struggling when circulating the classroom – can shave off valuable seconds with each pupil, making it easier to see every pupil in a lesson.[18] Addressing problems, mistakes and misconceptions in lessons is always preferable to doing it at another time. The added benefit of this approach is that it makes marking considerably quicker, as most of it has been done in the lesson.

However, in spite of our best efforts in a lesson, there will very often be one or more pupils who need additional support to be ready to move on to the next learning step with the rest of the class. Once you have identified these pupils, whether through your questioning, circulating during the lesson, or looking over their work immediately after lesson, you must decide what to teach them during an intervention session. Depending on when the intervention comes in the day, there will be different amounts of time to prepare for this session.

Some schools timetable keep-up intervention sessions to start immediately after the whole-class maths lesson, giving next to no time to formally prepare for these sessions, whereas other schools hold these sessions later in the day. Although the desired learning of this session will be the same as that of the main maths lesson which precedes it, it's important not to always simply reteach the same lesson again. While there may be times when this will be necessary and pupils just need a little more time and more intensive guidance from a teacher, there will also be times when pupils have not grasped a concept or procedure because of the way in which it was presented initially. At these times, it's important to approach the same learning in a different way, as there was clearly something the first time round that didn't help the pupils to understand, and this is unlikely to change if the same ideas are simply repeated. Using different representations to present the maths is a useful way of supporting pupils to develop understanding in this scenario.

The pupils who attend keep-up interventions will vary from day to day. This point is key to the way in which these interventions work, as they are supposed to respond to the changing needs of your pupils. We should teach our lessons, identify those who need more support, and intervene to provide this support to whoever needs it. Of course, there will be pupils who need to attend these sessions more regularly than others, as some pupils will generally be slower to grasp new ideas. The point is, though, that the pupils selected should always be there based on their performance in that day's lesson, rather than due to performance in previous lessons. There will be certain mathematical ideas that even pupils who are normally quick to grasp new learning will struggle with initially, and these pupils will require keep-up intervention from time to time too.

For this reason, ensure that your interventions truly are responding to needs identified in the lesson. If there are pupils who need more than a short keep-up intervention to grasp the lesson's learning, it's worth considering whether they should attend the keep-up session or instead whether they would be better supported through a catch-up intervention as described below. This will then allow you to focus on the pupils who do only require a little more help to be ready to move on to the next day's learning.

Keep-up interventions are challenging. In any intervention group there will be a number of pupils who haven't grasped the lesson's content but the reasons for this may vary. There will also be times when a large group of pupils don't seem to understand the lesson. In these situations, it can be difficult to decide whether to provide some additional instruction for a group of pupils or whether to reteach the whole class. There are obviously no hard-and-fast rules when making this decision (unless every child grasps the learning, or no one does!). However, I would suggest as a rule of thumb that if more than one third of a class appears to require intervention, it's worth strongly considering reteaching part or all of the lesson.

Catch-up interventions

There will undoubtedly be situations where certain pupils are unable to keep up with their peers, even with regular keep-up interventions. These pupils may have gaps in their understanding from previous learning which is holding them back or they may simply need to progress more slowly through new learning. In these situations, keep-up interventions may not be sufficient and a more structured approach, involving systematically going back to previous learning, may be required.

These catch-up interventions have a different purpose to keep-up interventions and therefore have a different structure. Catch-up interventions should be run with the same pupils for a set period of time to support them in catching up with their peers. Also, the learning in these sessions will not necessarily match the learning being taught in the current instructional sequence, as it may be that pupils require teaching from further back in the curriculum. In fact, it's very likely that the content of catch-up interventions will be quite different to what is being taught to the rest of the class.

The difficulty of catch-up interventions is that pupils who require them are likely to have different gaps in their understanding and thus need to go back over different things. Within any class, there will hopefully only be a small number of pupils who require this intervention. It's important to assess what gaps pupils may have in their prior learning to be able to address these gaps in a targeted way – there isn't time to go back to the beginning of the curriculum and simply reteach everything. Observing what these pupils can and can't do in maths lessons will give a good indication of where the gaps may be, and further questioning and assessment will help to identify exactly what the gaps are.

In an ideal world, we would take each pupil requiring a catch-up intervention and teach them individually, perfectly targeting their gaps. However, very few schools will have the capacity to do this unless they are lucky enough to have a surfeit of staff or a tiny number of pupils who are working below the level of their peers. In most other cases it will be necessary to group pupils based on the support that they need and the gaps in their understanding, and then teach them as a group. Having the pupils in these groups as close as possible in terms of what they need to learn will make teaching these sessions easier and more efficient, and running two smaller intervention groups where the pupils in each group have similar gaps in knowledge is likely to be preferable to running a single larger group. It may also be possible to start an intervention with a single pupil who has more significant gaps and then introduce other pupils to the group as you progress through the sessions.

Intervention logistics

Two questions that I'm often asked are 'when do you fit these interventions in?' and 'who will run them?'. Everyone working in schools knows that time is precious, and there is hardly time to fit in the lessons that we need to without adding in more. There are a number of different solutions to these difficulties which I'll outline below, and although it does depend on the school, I've never worked with a school, no matter how large or small, that has been unable to find sufficient time for these interventions.

First, let's answer the question about when these interventions should occur. One solution involves using curricular time normally devoted to other subjects. This is often an unpopular proposition. Pupils have the right to a full curriculum and taking them out of non-core lessons for extra maths teaching deprives them of this, the argument runs.

My counter-argument is always the same: pupils can't be allowed to leave primary school functionally innumerate. After being able to read and write, a solid foundation in mathematics is the most important right of every pupil, and so must be provided to every pupil, bar none. We must not allow the pupils who need more time and support – very often some of the most disadvantaged pupils in our schools – to leave at the end of Year 6 without a solid foundation in mathematics. To my mind, if that means these pupils miss parts of their non-core lessons from time to time, then this is a price worth paying, although I appreciate that some will disagree. Obviously, the ideal situation is that all pupils learn what they are taught the first time round so as to minimise the need for additional intervention, but we know that this doesn't happen in reality.

Another solution, used in many schools who do not have the staffing capacity to run interventions in lesson time, is to use assembly time for interventions. The assemblies are often run by senior leaders and teachers don't need to attend, giving them time to work with the pupil or pupils who need extra support.

The timings of these assemblies vary from school to school, but some schools have managed to organise the assembly to come straight after the maths lesson, allowing the lesson to flow straight into the intervention. This approach obviously requires the successful identification of pupils needing support to occur during the lesson. In other schools, these assemblies may be held later in the day, so there is a gap between the lesson and the intervention. This has the benefit of giving the teacher more time to look through activities completed by pupils to identify those who need more support and to pinpoint exactly what the barrier to learning might have been. In addition to this, it gives teachers more time to think about what the structure of the intervention will be.

Some schools have found other innovative ways of timetabling interventions. Some schools, rather than using assembly times, have used their teachers creatively, putting together classes for shorter sessions such as to hear a story, thus freeing up a teacher to run interventions. This approach works well in larger schools with multi-form entry. Some schools have even made use of staggered playtimes to allow time for interventions, freeing up different teachers at different times as necessary. The most practical method will depend on the particulars of each school – staffing, room availability, timetabling. Whatever method you choose to use, however, intervention is fundamental to teaching for mastery, and it's imperative to find sufficient time for it.

Now, let's look at the second question about who should deliver these interventions. The short answer is whoever is most mathematically knowledgeable and available to do so. In terms of keep-up interventions, whenever possible they should be run by the teacher who taught the initial lesson, as that teacher is likely to have the strongest understanding of what exactly the pupils weren't able to grasp. For catch-up interventions, the most important point is that they are delivered by the same person whenever possible, to ensure that the sequence of intervention sessions is as coherent as possible.

As a general rule, though, whatever the type of intervention, pupils who need more time or support to access their learning should be taught by the most qualified person possible. It's common practice in many schools to put the pupils who need the most help with the least qualified members of staff, often teaching assistants. This is not to denigrate teaching assistants at all – I've worked with some superb TAs in my time as a teacher, TAs who have made a huge difference to the education provided to pupils. However, it's normally the case that they are less well-qualified than teachers. Similarly, if there is a choice between teachers to run an intervention, I would always choose the more experienced teacher, or the teacher with the greatest level of mathematical pedagogical content knowledge. Pupils who need additional intervention require the best possible teaching, and this will generally be provided by the most experienced and qualified member of staff.

Intervention: key points

- Pupils will sometimes require intervention to support them with their learning. They may need more time or more support to grasp the learning.

- Keep-up interventions are designed to give pupils more time to grasp a particular lesson's learning, making sure they are ready to move on with the rest of their peers in the next lesson.

- A keep-up intervention should be carried out on the same day as the lesson it is based upon, and should be led by the teacher who taught the initial lesson wherever possible. Anyone who needs the additional instruction time should be able to attend the intervention, rather than there being a predetermined list of pupils.

- Catch-up interventions are for pupils who have gaps in their prior learning which are holding them back. These sessions are designed to help pupils catch up with their peers and should occur outside the time of the regular maths lesson as they are not linked to particular lessons in the way that keep-up interventions are.

- While timetabling interventions can be tricky, it's well worth finding a regular time that works for them, as they can be a powerful tool for ensuring that all pupils grasp the learning fully.

16 Delivering a learning step

Once you have planned your learning steps, you can then begin to deliver the content in your maths lessons. As we have seen, a learning step is not the same as a lesson; a single learning step may span multiple lessons and a single lesson could even contain more than one learning step. However, it's important to bear in mind that your time will still be divided into lessons, and so it's important to consider how your learning steps will fit into your allotted lesson time.

Lesson structure

There is no such thing as an ideal lesson structure. It is entirely dependent on a number of factors, including where you are in a particular learning step or instructional sequence, the relative expertise of your pupils in terms of the content, and your aims for the particular lesson. As discussed in Chapter 11, it can be useful to start a lesson with some proximal review, linking what pupils already know to the new learning that will take place in the lesson, but beyond this, there is no perfect structure for a lesson.

Three-part lessons remain in vogue in many schools, but this structure is often not supportive of pupils' learning, with starters and plenaries unrelated to the key learning taking up a significant proportion of the lesson time. What I would recommend instead is a multi-part lesson that alternates between the teacher teaching and the pupils doing. This back-and-forth approach is useful for a number of reasons. Firstly, it helps you as the teacher to structure your lessons, breaking the learning into small steps which you teach to your pupils one by one. Secondly, it allows you to assess how your pupils are coping with each of these steps, identifying difficulties as you go. Thirdly, it allows you to keep your pupils together, rather than more confident pupils simply racing off and causing large gaps to form within the class. Everyone moves together through the learning.

Activities

Every learning step should have an activity – a set of questions designed to ensure that pupils have successfully understood the content of the learning step. It's useful to think of your activity as the exit point for each learning step, demonstrating that pupils have sufficiently grasped the content of the step to be ready to move on. In the way that I recommended planning backwards when designing an instructional sequence, doing the same when planning a learning step is useful too. By designing an activity as your end point for a learning step, it's possible to work backwards from this to work out what teaching you will have to do to help your pupils to get there. The next section of the book will look in more detail at activity design.

Modelling, guided practice and completion questions

When teaching a new procedure, it's important to break it down into small steps and to allow pupils to practise each part. Through modelling, we can help pupils to learn each step, demonstrating the procedure and carefully explaining our thinking aloud as we model. Clear modelling of an example question should be followed by guided practice: examples where we talk pupils through the steps of a question, modelling at the same time if necessary. This stage of learning a procedure by doing it alongside an expert is crucial, but it's a stage in many lessons that is rushed through too quickly or sometimes skipped altogether.

Once pupils have engaged in guided practice, they should be given opportunities to answer completion problems (partially solved questions with one or more steps missed out). Pupils must complete the missing step to complete the problem. It's most effective to start with just the final step missing, meaning pupils only have one thing to complete, then work back through the steps one at a time, until pupils are able to solve the entire problem.

Practice

Early in my career, I would often give my pupils reams of calculations so they could practise what they'd learned. While not bad in itself, this focus meant that I built precious little time for problem solving and reasoning into my lessons. As I developed my teaching and started to understand the importance of these elements, I vastly decreased the number of calculation questions in my lessons, reasoning that if my pupils could successfully answer a small number of questions then they probably didn't need to answer a great deal more. Unfortunately, the pendulum had swung too far the other way.

Now, I take a more moderate approach. There is much more to maths than pupils simply being able to answer lots of calculations, and the questions and activities that we devise for our pupils should contain a variety of rich and interesting questions. But children learn through practice, so it's still important that we give our pupils the opportunity to practise what we're teaching them. For this reason, it's important that our lessons allow for this practice, as well as the carefully designed activities that the next section of this book will describe.

Delivering a learning step: key points

- While there is no ideal lesson structure, most lessons should start with some kind of proximal review, linking previous learning to the new learning to come.

- Broadly speaking, an approach of alternating small sections of teaching with opportunities for pupils to do examples for themselves can allow the class to progress through the learning together.

- When teaching a new procedure, teacher modelling, followed by guided practice and completion tasks, allows pupils to break complex procedures down into clear steps that they can learn one by one.

- Opportunities for pupils to practise these procedures with multiple examples will help to reinforce your pupils' learning.

- Each learning step should have a clear end point – a well-designed activity which demonstrates to you that pupils have learned what was intended. The activity should be completed independently by pupils to demonstrate their ability to answer a variety of questions, signalling whether you can move on to the next learning step.

Section 3 Activity design

The following chapters will look at the key elements to consider when designing an activity (a series of questions for your pupils to answer). Every learning step should have some kind of activity for pupils to complete, and it's important to consider the purpose of this activity. It's easy to think of the activities we design and the questions we ask pupils as being our assessment of what they've learned in a lesson, but as we've seen, learning takes place over time and can't be judged in a single lesson. The real test of whether something has been learned is whether it has been retained weeks, months and years down the line, not whether pupils can do something immediately after they've been taught it. As previously discussed, this is the distinction between 'performance' and 'learning'. Performance is whether newly taught procedural knowledge can be correctly used at the time or soon after it's been taught, whereas learning is whether this knowledge becomes integrated into long-term memory and can be correctly used further down the line. Performance is no guarantor of learning.

As we've seen in previous chapters, previously learned material must be revisited and practised in order for it to be integrated into long-term memory. At the same time, newly taught material must be practised in order for it to be retained in the first place. Therefore, we must ensure that the activities we design serve two functions:

- to acquire and practise newly taught knowledge
- to recall and practise previously taught knowledge.

Bearing in mind these two linked, though distinct, functions when planning activities will ensure that pupils are always engaged in purposeful practice that will help them to learn in the long term.

There is an important point to make before we look at the details of how to design an activity: it is well worth writing your own sets of questions for pupils rather than only relying on questions written by someone else. While I'm sure that all teachers at one point or another have relied on something found on the internet, maybe from Primary Resources, TES or elsewhere, writing your own questions is one of the most rewarding and high-leverage uses of your time as a teacher. You are the teacher, you know what the intended learning of the lesson is, and you should design questions to support this intention. Using someone else's questions will not allow you to match the questions to the learning. Downloading a set of questions may save some time, but not much, and it is certainly not worth the trade-off. The regularity with which you do this will depend on a number of factors – teachers who frequently use a textbook to teach may have less opportunity to do this than others, for example – but whenever you have the opportunity to do so, write your own questions.

In the coming chapters, we'll look at how the three stated purposes of maths education outlined in the English National Curriculum – fluency, reasoning and problem solving – can be considered when planning activities, whilst also thinking about how we can scaffold learning for those pupils who are slower to grasp the learning, and how we can ensure that the learning we build is deep. Pulling all of these elements together will help you to build high-quality activities for your maths lessons.

A final point about activities: I use the term 'activity' to refer to a piece of work at the end of a learning step which is your ideal end point for that step. Please bear in mind that this activity is not the only work your pupils will be completing. You will use examples, models, guided questions and completion problems in your lessons. You may give a number of questions practising a newly-learned procedure. You will use quizzes and tests too. An activity, as I have defined it, is only one type of task that your pupils will complete in your lessons – it's just a particularly important one.

17 Mathematical fluency

The National Curriculum in England (2014) identifies three aims for maths education: fluency, mathematical reasoning and problem solving.[19] These three elements should therefore run throughout your instructional sequences to ensure that your pupils are able to gain a full understanding of the mathematics that they are taught. We will look at what each of these elements refers to in turn, before considering how and in which proportions you can include them in your instructional sequences. Let's start by considering fluency.

Fluency

> 'The National Curriculum for mathematics aims to ensure that all pupils:
>
> become **fluent** in the fundamentals of mathematics, including through varied and frequent practice with increasingly complex problems over time, so that pupils develop conceptual understanding and the ability to recall and apply knowledge rapidly and accurately'
>
> (National Curriculum in England, 2014)

Mathematical fluency is the ability to be effective at mathematical endeavours through having a well-developed knowledge of procedures, relationships and concepts. Fluency is sometimes characterised as being able to calculate quickly, but there is more to it than just this. To use the analogy of someone who is fluent in a second language, fluency is more than simply having a wide vocabulary and a well-practised ability to conjugate verbs correctly (although these are necessary for fluency). True fluency is knowing the language inside out, having an awareness of when a word or phrase is appropriate and when it is not and drawing on your entire knowledge of the language to make a decision about what to say and how to say it. Fluency is not a fixed point that you reach, it's a direction on a continuum that you work towards. Exactly the same is true for mathematics. Susan Russell, a mathematics educator, has identified three key components for computational fluency: accuracy, efficiency and flexibility.[20] Let's consider each of these in turn and put them together in order to build up a picture of what a mathematically fluent pupil looks like.

Accuracy is the ability to recall facts – such as multiplication facts or number bonds – and to use procedures with minimal effort or conscious thought while achieving a very high success rate. This includes the ability to check answers accurately too. Accuracy comes through repeated practice of recalling facts and using procedures, with the aim that it eventually becomes automatic. This is where some teachers' idea of fluency ends, but this is in fact where it starts. Accurate recall and calculation are the basis of fluency, not its ultimate goal.

Efficiency is the ability to use a procedure to solve a problem in a way that uses minimal steps, so the pupil doesn't become stuck or lose track of what they are doing. A deep knowledge of the relationships between numbers and operations (such as knowing that if $4 + 6 = 10$ then $0.4 + 0.6 = 1$, or knowing that addends can be added in any order, for example) is an important element of efficiency. It's common for pupils who are developing their fluency to work in ways that lack efficiency, even if they are accurate. For example, a pupil answering a question such as 19 x 7 by adding seven to itself nineteen times is clearly being inefficient, even though this would result in the correct answer, providing no mistakes were made.

Flexibility is the ability to select from a range of efficient strategies to choose the best one for the job. An important element in the acquisition of flexibility is being given the chance to compare and critique different strategies to answer questions, while considering which makes the most sense. A common example that demonstrates a lack of flexibility is a pupil choosing to answer a question such as 998 x 7 by using the standard algorithm (long multiplication) rather than seeing that the answer will simply be 14 less than 7,000. This lack of flexibility is a common deficit in terms of pupils' fluency.

Mathematical fluency sits at the nexus of these three elements. A pupil who is given opportunities to develop accuracy, efficiency and flexibility will develop in their mathematical fluency. This development is a never-ending journey of improvement that all learners should be taken on. You can take pupils on this journey by ensuring that you provide them with a wide variety of questions to answer which have been chosen carefully in order to develop accuracy, efficiency and flexibility.

Questions which develop fluency

From the above description, you can see that the sort of questions which develop fluency are not fixed – they depend on where each pupil is in their own mathematical learning. Therefore, questions which develop fluency will look very different at different times, but there should be a focus on pupils developing their accuracy first. Questions that develop accuracy should come early on in an instructional sequence, especially ones that allow pupils to practise prerequisite procedures.

For instance, when teaching an instructional sequence on angle geometry, the ability to add and subtract several two and three digit numbers successfully would absolutely be a prerequisite. Presuming that this has already been assessed and pupils are able to do this, practice of the procedure will help to build up pupils' accuracy and automaticity. This will be important when pupils are answering questions where their attention needs to be directed to other areas (such as selecting which values should be used to calculate with). In short, questions which will develop fluency through a focus on accuracy will:

- Give pupils the opportunity to practise known procedures and to recall known facts which are relevant to the instructional sequence.
- Allow them to recall and to practise newly-learned knowledge regularly, so that it starts to become embedded in their long-term memory.

The speed at which pupils are able to develop accuracy of a particular procedure is largely dependent upon its complexity, hence the importance of breaking down an instructional sequence into small and coherent steps. The use of completion problems is an excellent way of breaking down a procedure into sub-steps, enabling pupils to develop fluency in each sub-step before moving on to the next. For example, pupils who are learning to add pairs of numbers which involve regrouping may first answer questions that just involve regrouping in the ones, to develop accuracy in that procedure.

Once pupils have become sufficiently accurate at a newly learned procedure, it's important to shift the focus of the questions to efficiency and flexibility. This means that these sorts of questions will come slightly later in the instructional sequence, as accuracy must start to be established first. If pupils can't answer questions accurately, there is little point in them developing their efficiency and flexibility – we don't want our pupils to develop a flexible range of efficient methods that are incorrect.

Questions seeking to develop pupils' efficiency and flexibility should be designed to draw their attention to the relationships that exist between numbers, concepts and procedures. We've already identified ways of doing this in Chapter 13 on procedural variation, where we saw how careful question choice could be used to draw pupils' attention to specific ideas. For example, when pupils are learning to move from a 'count all' to a 'count on' strategy as part of early addition, the following sets of calculations could be very helpful in terms of developing pupils' efficiency:

$$12 + 2 =$$

$$14 + 5 =$$

$$17 + 3 =$$

$$3 + 17 =$$

$$5 + 14 =$$

$$2 + 12 =$$

Pupils who are solving this set of questions on a number line by starting on the first addend and counting on the second could have their attention drawn to two very important principles: firstly, that starting with the larger of the two addends and counting on the smaller is vastly more efficient, and crucially, that it gives us exactly the same result. This early exposure to the benefits of the commutative law is incredibly powerful.

A set of questions that draw pupils' attention to key information about multiplication could look like this:

$$98 \times 8 =$$

$$99 \times 8 =$$

$$100 \times 8 =$$

$$101 \times 8 =$$

$$102 \times 8 =$$

These questions illustrate how each product increases by eight because there is one more 'lot' of eight each time. By drawing pupils' attention to this over the course of several questions, we can demonstrate that if we have a multiplication question where one factor is close to the power of ten (10, 100, 1,000, etc.) we can use a compensatory method, i.e. multiply and then adjust. This is one of many different scenarios that we should be teaching our pupils to recognise and exploit.

Below, I've listed some of the key knowledge that pupils should have which will encourage them to work with flexibility and efficiency, and included a brief explanation as to why each piece of knowledge is so important. This knowledge can be developed through the questions that we ask our pupils to answer, drawing their attention to salient points once they have done so.

An understanding of the commutative, associative and distributive laws

This knowledge gives pupils the ability to manipulate calculations in order to answer them more efficiently. For example, knowing that multiplication is both commutative and associative allows pupils to solve a calculation such as 4 x 7 x 5 by assessing the different options for solving it: choosing to multiply either 4 and 7, 4 and 5, or 7 and 5 first, before multiplying the product by the remaining factor. This flexibility couldn't be demonstrated by pupils unaware of these laws.

An ability to derive number facts additively and multiplicatively

Pupils need a great deal of practice to be able to derive new facts from known facts. It's important they are able to do this for all four operations, both additively and multiplicatively. By this, I mean that pupils must know what happens to the answer of any calculation when any of the terms is changed by either addition, subtraction, multiplication or division. For example, knowing that if 15 x 3 = 45, then 15 x 30 = 450, or that if 60 − 14 = 46, then 60 − 24 = 36. This sort of knowledge will allow them to put to use a relatively small number of known key facts.

An ability to manipulate calculations

Pupils who have a knowledge of the commutative law (as described above) will know that the order of the addends in an addition equation and the factors in a multiplication equation can be changed without affecting the sum or product respectively:

$$6 + 13 = 13 + 6$$

$$5 \times 8 = 8 \times 5$$

However, pupils should also know all equations can be manipulated in order to clarify the relationships between the parts. For example, division and subtraction equations can be rearranged when the relationships between the terms in the equation are understood:

$$42 \div 7 = 6$$

$$42 \div 6 = 7$$

$$39 - 8 = 31$$

$$39 - 31 = 8$$

This knowledge also needs to be extended into a clear understanding of the relationship between addition and subtraction, and multiplication and division. For example:

$$17 + 21 = 36$$

$$36 - 21 = 17$$

$$12 \times 3 = 36$$

$$36 \div 3 = 12$$

This knowledge is important for pupils to be able to solve 'empty box problems', for example knowing that $5 + x = 13$ can be rearranged to $13 - 5 = x$.

An ability to factorise

Pupils should be able to readily factorise numbers to be able to work flexibly and efficiently. This ability allows pupils to answer the following question more easily:

$$25 \times 24 =$$

Knowing that 24 can be factorised into 4 and 6 allows the calculation to be reconstituted as $25 \times 4 \times 6$, and thus 100×6. This is much more efficient than using the standard algorithm for multiplication. However, knowing to factorise 24 into 4 and 6 rather than any other factor pair brings me on to the final point.

Knowledge of pairs of numbers which add or multiply to make powers of ten

The knowledge of number pairs that add or multiply to make 'round' numbers (generally understood to be powers of ten and their multiples) is very important, as the last example showed. We tend to focus on number bonds to 10 and 100, but multiplication facts are just as important. I've included most of the key facts below. Along with these known facts, the ability to derive new facts from all of these is obviously essential too.

Addition facts

$$1 + 9$$

$$2 + 8$$

$$3 + 7$$

$$4 + 6$$

$$5 + 5$$

Multiplication facts

$$2 \times 5$$

$$4 \times 5$$

$$5 \times 5$$

$$4 \times 25$$

$$8 \times 12.5$$

With these facts, pupils will be able to identify opportunities for efficient and flexible working within other questions that they're answering.

One final point to make about mathematical fluency is that it's not analogous to simply practising calculations. There is sometimes an inaccurate dichotomy imagined between fluency and problem solving, in that fluency always consists of raw numerical calculations and problem solving consists only of worded problems. This is not the case, even if it does sometimes prove to be true. Take the following two questions:

A. $15 \times 16 =$

B.   Pencils are sold in packs of five. If I buy eight packs, how many pencils do I have in total?

At first sight, many might conclude that question A is a question to develop fluency whereas question B is a problem-solving question. I would argue that this is not the case, and either question could be categorised in either way, depending entirely on pupils' existing knowledge and where the questions came in an instructional sequence.

Question A could be a question that develops a pupil's fluency if it were given at a point where they had learned how to multiply two-digit numbers. The pupil would need an understanding of the distributive law, solid knowledge of times table facts and a secure method to use to answer the question. If a pupil had not had experience of multiplying pairs of two-digit numbers, this question would still be solvable with knowledge of times tables and a rudimentary understanding of the concept of multiplication. However, the question would then be much more akin to a problem solving question, without a clear means of finding an answer, an efficient method or methods to select from, or a means of checking accuracy. Answering a question like this would be unlikely to help the pupil to develop their mathematical fluency. This shows how the same question can be used to develop different skills depending on how and when it is used.

Similarly, question B would be categorised by many as a problem-solving question. This may well be the case for pupils who haven't encountered this sort of question before, perhaps those who are in the embryonic stages of learning about multiplication. They may have to draw pictures, read and reread the question, or count effortfully in ones to find a solution. However, for learners who have a little more experience in multiplication, this sort of question would absolutely be one that develops fluency: it's the most prevalent, simple and boring (although no less important for it) linguistic representation of multiplication that there is. This is the sort of question that we would want every single pupil to quickly recognise and then be able to solve in their sleep. Again, the same question, but different purposes depending on when it is used in an instructional sequence.

The key pattern here is that as pupils become increasingly proficient in and knowledgeable about any area of maths, the proportion of questions that will be problems – in the sense of being unfamiliar and without a set routine to solve them – will decrease. As an instructional sequence progresses, questions that may have been 'problems' earlier in the sequence will become increasingly familiar to pupils and will start to build fluency, increasing the ability to answer with automaticity. Your ultimate aim for your pupils should be that they become fluent in all the areas of maths that we teach them in primary school, enabling them to go on to become successful mathematicians in the future.

Fluency: key points

- The National Curriculum for England identifies three key strands of mathematics that pupils should be taught to develop: fluency, reasoning and problem solving.

- Fluency is the ability to work with accuracy, efficiency and flexibility to solve mathematical problems.

- Questions that we select for pupils to answer, and the subsequent discussions that we should have with pupils about the methods used, should be designed to develop pupils' accuracy, efficiency and flexibility.

- Fluency in mathematics develops over time and is not just limited to pupils who are earlier on in their mathematical learning. Any new learning in maths, from the incredibly simple to the incredibly complex, will require purposeful practice in order to develop fluency.

- Identifying whether or not a question will develop fluency has little to do with the question itself and a great deal to do with what a pupil already knows about the mathematical domain.

18 Problem solving

After having considered how you can develop fluency, let's now look at another aim of the mathematics curriculum in England: problem solving.

'The National Curriculum for mathematics aims to ensure that all pupils:

- *can* **solve problems** *by applying their mathematics to a variety of routine and non-routine problems with increasing sophistication, including breaking down problems into a series of simpler steps and persevering in seeking solutions'*

(National Curriculum in England, 2014)

A key element of maths education is developing pupils' ability to solve mathematical problems. If our pupils don't become proficient problem-solvers, we're not really teaching them mathematics. Although our job as primary teachers is to secure pupils' knowledge of mathematical fundamentals, an important part of doing this is giving them the ability to solve problems.

As we saw in the last chapter, there is considerable overlap between problem solving and developing fluency, and much of the distinction between them depends on the pupils that we're teaching, what their prior knowledge is and where they are in a particular instructional sequence. The exact definition of a mathematical problem is not universally agreed upon, but it's often defined simply as a mathematical question that requires an answer. I think that this definition is so broad as to be not particularly useful. Therefore, the definition of a mathematical 'problem' that I'll use in this book is a question where pupils don't immediately recognise a tried and tested method for finding a solution. This definition is certainly broader than the narrow view of problem solving that only refers to 'word problems'.

Problem solving is a difficult thing to teach. For a long time, I believed that problem solving was a generic skill and that the ability to solve problems could be applied across subjects and disciplines, as well as across different domains within a discipline. I now don't believe this to be true. However, much of problem solving advice still acts as if this *is* true. Take the RUCSAC approach to problem solving:

R **READ:** Read the question. What is the important information?

U **UNDERSTAND:** Understand the question. What do you need to find out?

C **CHOOSE:** Choose the correct method of calculation to answer the question.

S **SOLVE:** Solve the problem. Make sure you follow the steps.

A **ANSWER:** Answer the question. What were you meant to find out?

C **CHECK:** Check your answer. Use the inverse to check your working.

Figure 17

This misleading approach implies that all problems can be solved in the same generic way (see Figure 17). Let's look at some of the problems with this particular approach.

Telling our pupils to read and understand the problem is not helpful at all. We can't just choose to understand a problem or not. There is no magic switch in our heads that we can turn on. Either we understand what a question is asking, or we don't. If we don't understand the question, we aren't then able to choose the right operation as we don't know what to do. In terms of the last three steps, they are obvious if we know what to do, impossible if we don't. RUCSAC doesn't offer us help to solve problems; it is a post hoc description of what we probably did if we solved a problem correctly.

The hurdle that we fall at when trying to solve an unfamiliar problem is that of understanding the question. We can't just understand any problem that we're presented with. We build up our expertise of solving problems through the gradual accumulation of knowledge within a particular subject domain. This point is important. For example, I could become relatively expert at solving problems involving the four operations, but still be a novice in solving geometrical problems. We learn to solve problems *within a particular domain* by having a deep well of knowledge of that area and by having had practice at solving increasingly complex problems within that area, guided by expert teachers.

Look at this example problem from NCETM:[21]

Each shape stands for a number. The numbers shown are the totals of the line of four numbers in the row or column. Find the remaining totals.

Δ	Ø	Δ	Ω	
Ø	Ω	Ø	Δ	25
Ω	Ω	Ω	Ω	20
Δ	Ø	Ø	Δ	
			26	

Figure 18

When I first saw this problem, I was quickly able to solve it.

- I knew that I needed to look for a single symbol repeated a number of times to make up a known value. I expected to see this, because this would be the most obvious way to solve the puzzle.

- This led me to the third row. I knew that dividing 20 by 4 would give me the value of 'Ω', 5.

- I then knew that I should look for another known value which was made up of 'Ω' and only one other symbol.

- This led me to the fourth column. I knew that subtracting 10 (two Ωs) from 26 and dividing the answer by 2 (the number of Δs in the column) would give me the value of Δ (8).

- I then knew that the third known value (25) would allow me to calculate the value of $\emptyset$ by subtracting 13 ($\Omega + \Delta$) and dividing by 2.

- Having established that $\emptyset = 6$, I could then find the unknown values of the other rows and columns by simple arithmetic. I did all of this in less than a minute.

The key thing to understand here is that my ability to rapidly solve the problem existed because I had seen variations of this problem before. I had knowledge of the type of problem and had had practice of solving very similar problems. It was not down to any kind of generic problem-solving ability. This is why I struggled when I first came across the following problem:

> *Jake can paint a room in 6 hours, whereas it would only take Sam 3 hours to paint the same room. If Jake and Sam both painted the room together, how long would it take them?*

When I first encountered this problem, I found myself to be stuck. While being stuck can be frustrating, it is a common stage of problem solving, and does not mean that the problem you are facing is unsolvable. Indeed, the excellent book *Thinking Mathematically* talks a great deal about the importance of being stuck and is a must-read for mathematics educators.[22]

At first, I couldn't find a way 'in' to the problem; indeed, it seemed at first that I didn't even have enough information to solve the problem. After much pondering, I found my way in to the problem by realising that I could consider the rate at which each of the painters painted, and thinking about what fraction of the room would be painted after particular lengths of time. So, after one hour, Jake would have painted $\frac{1}{6}$ of the room, while Sam would have painted of $\frac{1}{3}$ the room. $\frac{1}{3} = \frac{2}{6}$, so after one hour, a total of $\frac{3}{6}$ of the room would have been painted. $\frac{3}{6} = \frac{1}{2}$, so in total it would have taken them 2 hours to paint the entire room.

I wasn't able to solve this problem initially because *I had never seen anything like it*. Its structure was new to me, and I had no knowledge, frame of reference or prototypical example with which to compare it. It was not that I was a poor problem-solver, I just had no knowledge of this type of problem. Even though I did manage to solve it eventually, I emphasise again that the ability to do so was not due to a generic problem-solving 'skill'; it was actually down to my domain knowledge of fractions. I realised that I could work out the 'fraction of the room per hour' and work from there. If I didn't have a good knowledge of the domain of fractions, the lightbulb moment probably wouldn't have come, and I may never have become unstuck and been able to solve the problem.

How to write mathematical problems

When planning an activity, it is important to ensure that *all* of your pupils will have the opportunity to engage in problem-solving. Too often, problem-solving comes only at the end of a lesson or instructional sequence, saved for the pupils who progress through the rest of the work most quickly. Problem-solving must not only be the preserve of these pupils – it is an essential part of mathematics for everyone. When designing activities and writing problems, therefore, you should ensure that problem-solving is accessible to all by creating problems with varying levels of difficulty which can be spread throughout your activities. This can be done in a couple of key ways: firstly by considering the problem's deep structure and secondly by considering the problem's surface structure.

A problem's deep structure refers to the actual mathematics that pupils will have to engage in to solve the problem. What is the procedure, algorithm or set of steps that will be necessary to answer the problem? We can vary the difficulty of a problem that we create by varying the difficulty of the underlying mathematics necessary to solve it. By doing this, we can ensure that our pupils are presented with a range of levels of difficulty in the problems that we present them with. Bear in mind that it can be very challenging for pupils to problem-solve when they are only just beginning to become fluent in the underlying mathematics. This problem can be counteracted by creating problems where the deep structure is simpler, potentially from previous instructional sequences or year groups.

As well as changing the difficulty of a problem's deep structure, we can also alter the difficulty of a problem's surface structure too. This refers to the problem as it is first presented – it is the surface structure that initially conceals the deep structure and is what makes a problem a problem, at least by my definition. There will be some surface structures which are easy to penetrate and others which are more opaque initially. The difficulty partly depends on pupils' familiarity with the surface structure, as seen in problems above, and regular problem-solving practice can help to make pupils more familiar with many common surface structures.

So, to write effective problems, consider the deep structure of the problem first – what is the mathematics that you want your pupils to do? Then, consider the surface structure of the problem – how will you present the underlying mathematics to them? The more unusual the surface structure, the harder the problem is likely to be to solve. To widen your own repertoire of surface structures that you can employ when writing problems, seek out a range of problems written by others: test papers, textbooks, websites. The more unique and interesting problems you encounter yourself, the better you will become at devising your own problems.

How to teach problem solving

So how should we teach problem solving? In order to solve problems effectively, we can see that our pupils need two things:

- experience of a wide range of problem types that pupils have had success in solving
- strong domain knowledge of different areas of mathematics.

With these two elements, we can ensure that when pupils encounter mathematical problems, either in our classrooms or in the future, they will have a high degree of success in knowing how to solve them. In addition to this, it's vital to remember that successful problem solving is built on a foundation of computational fluency, to the point where calculation has become automatic. We know that pupils' working memories can quickly become overloaded if they need to attend to multiple things at once, and if their attention is split by having to (a) work out what to do to solve a problem and (b) do the actual mathematics required to solve it, then they are likely to make errors in their working. When pupils' ability to calculate is near-automatic, they will be able to focus all of their attention on the problem at hand.

Teaching problem solving is made easier by taking the 'backwards planning' approach discussed earlier in the book (see page 27). By deciding on the sorts of problems that we want our pupils to be able to answer at the end of an instructional sequence, we can work backwards and identify appropriate places for problem solving earlier in the sequence. Because of the importance of fluency for problem solving, I find that it usually makes sense to spend less time on problem solving earlier in an instructional sequence and more time on it later, once fluency has started to become embedded (see Figure 19).

When teaching problem solving, I'll typically present an example problem and give pupils time to read and consider the problem. If this is a problem they're unlikely to have encountered before, I won't ask them to attempt to solve it. I know that doing so is an approach used by many, but my feeling is that I want them to see a modelled example before they have a go themselves. Once the pupils have considered the problem, I'll ask some questions, typically along the lines of 'What do we know?', 'What do we need to find?' and 'What maths knowledge does it look we will need to use?'. Having taken answers to these questions and given pupils the opportunity to build on each other's answers, I'll start to solve the problem. I'll do this by working on the whiteboard and explaining my thinking as I go along. Depending on the complexity of the problem, I may make a note of the steps too, giving each step a short name.

Having completed the problem, I'll model how to check that my solution correctly solved the problem. Then it will be the pupils' turn to solve a similar problem. This problem will have the same deep structure as my worked example, but often have a different surface context. I'll explicitly tell my pupils that the problems have the same structure and require the same steps to solve. Leaving my worked example on the board, I'll proceed through the steps one by one, asking pupils to complete each step separately, one at a time. After each step, I'll ask a pupil to describe what they did for that step, and again I'll model it myself on the whiteboard.

At this point, the pupils have seen one modelled example and worked through one problem themselves, one step at a time. I'll then ask pupils to try a third question with the same deep structure themselves, but this time without breaking it down into separate steps. Again, I'll remind them that the problem follows the same pattern as the previous ones.

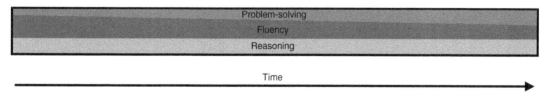

Figure 19

This very structured method of teaching problem-solving ensures that pupils are exposed to a wide range of problems that have varying contexts and surface structures but the same deep structure, and that they've seen, step by step, how an expert solves them. This is how I suggest teaching problem solving to pupils. Having said that, it's incredibly important that once you've worked through complex problems with your pupils, you give them the opportunity to problem-solve independently. To do this, I ensure that I give pupils varied examples of problems when I design my activities, including examples of problems they've encountered before but perhaps with a different surface structure. Doing this regularly ensures that pupils are given the opportunity to tackle a range of problems, which helps them to incrementally develop their expertise in choosing the appropriate method to solve problems they encounter in the future.

Problem solving: key points

- Problem solving is central to learning mathematics. If we don't teach our pupils to problem-solve, we're not really teaching them mathematics.

- There is no such thing as a generic problem-solving ability. Being good at solving problems in one domain does not make you good at solving problems in another. (I'm quite good at solving mathematical problems but I'm not so good at solving plumbing ones, as I don't have enough knowledge of the domain of plumbing!)

- Pupils need experience of a wide variety of problems, being shown worked examples before attempting to answer them on their own.

- Pupils also need strong domain knowledge of the different areas of the maths curriculum to enable them to solve problems in different domains.

- Mathematical problem solving relies on mathematical fluency. If pupils can't calculate fluently, their working memory is likely to be taken up with this, stopping them from really focusing on the problem itself.

- Giving pupils the opportunity to solve a wide range of problems with a deep structure they've encountered before allows them to develop their ability to choose the correct method to solve a problem.

19 Reasoning

The remaining aim of maths as outlined in the National Curriculum in England is to develop mathematical reasoning.

> 'The National Curriculum for mathematics aims to ensure that all pupils:
>
> - **reason mathematically** by following a line of enquiry, conjecturing relationships and generalisations, and developing an argument, justification or proof using mathematical language'
>
> (National Curriculum in England, 2014)

Maths is about far more than calculating the answers to questions and solving problems. It's also a discipline with its own ways of thinking and behaving, and mathematical reasoning is a key element of this. Reasoning is one of the least understood and infrequently included areas of maths for non-specialist teachers in primary schools.

Mathematical reasoning means having an awareness of how a particular problem was solved and understanding why it could be solved in that way. More than this, reasoning is also the ability to describe patterns and make generalisations, conjecturing about what may or may not happen in different situations. It's about being able to take a step back and look at a particular question from a bird's-eye view and clearly describe what is happening. A shorthand that I often use for reasoning is that it's about 'going beyond the answer', rather than simply finding out what the answer is. It often involves looking at special cases or generalising about questions that have been asked. For example, take the following question stem:

> 'There are some red and blue marbles in a bag. There are three times as many blue marbles as there are red marbles.'

We can consider this to be the set-up to a problem, as there is currently no question to answer; I have simply described a situation. Whether we're asking pupils to solve it or to reason about it depends on what we ask next. If our scenario continues…

'If there are 24 marbles altogether, how many blue marbles are there?'

…then we are asking our pupils to solve a problem, in that there's a particular solution we want them to find (there are 16 blue marbles). However, if we continue our scenario like this…

'Miriam says, "Whatever the number of red marbles, the total number of marbles will be even." Is Miriam correct? Explain why or why not.'

…then we are asking a question that encourages our pupils to reason mathematically. Different pupils would bring their knowledge and experience to this second kind of question in multiple different ways. For example, some may see quite quickly that this is essentially asking if all multiples of three are even. Others may see that it's incorrect by considering two elements: firstly, that any integer multiplied by two gives an even product, and secondly, that an odd number added to an even number will give you an odd sum. Other pupils are likely to answer the question through specialising – trying particular examples to see what happens. In doing this, working through examples systematically will quickly show the statement to be incorrect.

On top of actually working out whether the statement is incorrect, there is the matter of articulating the answer. Pupils might quickly realise that the statement is incorrect but having to explain and articulate this is a different matter altogether, although an equally important skill. In this example, pupils could prove the statement to be incorrect with a single example (e.g. three red marbles would give a total of nine marbles, which is an odd number). However, for some questions a longer explanation may be necessary. This comes back to building in opportunities for pupils to talk about and articulate learning in lessons, as pupils need regular teacher models and practice of their own for this to become second nature.

We can see then that a 'reasoning' question is quite different to a 'problem-solving' question, and it is also richer. While the problem-solving question above has a single answer which can be quickly calculated, the 'reasoning' version asks pupils to consider a number of different cases, test a suggested 'rule' and articulate their findings clearly. There's far more to be taken from the 'reasoning' question above than there is from the 'problem-solving' version. This is why it's important to build opportunities for mathematical reasoning into your lessons.

Having said that, it's important to remember that questions like the former must also have a place in your maths lessons. In spite of its simplicity, the first question is a prototypical example of much more complex questions about proportional reasoning that pupils must be able to work with. Also, it's important to note that pupils would need to be able to solve the first question to be able to tackle the second: if they can't work out what will happen in a single case, they won't be able to compare what happens in multiple cases. Furthermore, there's absolutely no reason why you couldn't ask them the first question and then follow up with the second. Both are important and each serves its own purpose.

Questions which develop reasoning

We've seen that it's important to build in opportunities for reasoning throughout your teaching. Reasoning should be an integral part of maths lessons and should run through all your instructional sequences. I tend to keep the proportion of reasoning I use in my learning steps fairly constant throughout an instructional sequence, while varying the relative proportions of fluency and problem-solving questions:

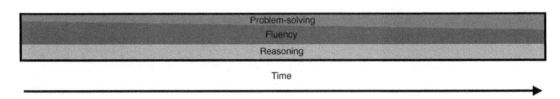

Time

Figure 20

This is because pupils are able to demonstrate their mathematical reasoning with questions of any difficulty. Pupils should always be expected to talk about how they got to a certain answer, to make conjectures about what might happen in a different situation, or to challenge the thinking of others. This is what I think of as the 'informal reasoning' that should become a regular part of our toolkit as teachers.

The easiest way to do this is by asking 'how' and 'why' questions of your pupils when they give you solutions to problems. These questions have a threefold purpose. Firstly, they get pupils into the habit of articulating themselves, using mathematical vocabulary and language to explain their thinking. Secondly, it's a means of checking on pupils' mathematical knowledge, interrogating their understanding of the maths rather than simply being happy with a correct answer (which may have been copied from someone else), a lucky guess, or the result of something only partially understood. Thirdly, asking 'how' and 'why' regularly builds a habit in our pupils – if they come to expect these questions at all times, they will eventually begin to ask these questions of themselves without being prompted.

In terms of more formal reasoning, there are a number of activities which prompt pupils to delve deeper into their answers and to think more deeply about the maths. Some of the following question stems are ideal for getting pupils to start to reason effectively.

- **'What do you notice?'** A broad question, but a powerful one that you should be asking regularly in maths lessons. As mentioned in Chapter 7 on big ideas, patterns are everywhere in maths, and training our pupils to notice things is an important way to develop mathematical thinking. Pupils will typically notice a whole host of different things, some pertinent, some less so. Supplementary questions, such as 'What do you notice about x?' can then narrow down the focus to what you as the teacher are interested in.

  Example: Look at the following division calculations:

  $10 \div 3 = 3 \text{ r}1$

  $11 \div 3 = 3 \text{ r}2$

  $12 \div 3 = 4$

  $13 \div 3 = 4 \text{ r}1$

  $14 \div 3 = 4 \text{ r}2$

  $15 \div 3 = 5$

  What do you notice?

- **'What would happen if…?'** This is a very effective question as it forces pupils to examine change and patterns, and to make conjectures about what might happen. Again, this is a question that we want our pupils to start considering themselves, as it represents another very mathematical way of thinking. Regularly asking this of our pupils builds the habit of thinking in this way.

  Example: We know that $24 \div 6 = 4$. What would happen if we doubled the divisor? What if we doubled it again?

- **True or false/always, sometimes or never?** Both of these question types are very useful as they force pupils to think more generally, rather than just considering the particular case in front of them. This is another key element of mathematical thinking.

   Example: The sum of any three odd numbers will be odd. True or false?

The NCETM has produced progression maps that lay out the National Curriculum domains and identify opportunities for reasoning with concrete question examples. Using some of these questions as part of your lessons on a regular basis is an excellent way of ensuring that you build in plenty of opportunities for reasoning into your maths lessons. They can be found on the NCETM website.[23] They will also prove a useful reference when designing your own questions along similar lines.

Progression in reasoning

The NRICH primary team have written a great deal on reasoning, and a number of NRICH problems promote mathematical reasoning. In one article, they articulate a progression in reasoning that pupils will go through as they develop their ability to reason.[24] They identify five stages of reasoning:

STEP 1
Describing: *simply tells what they did.*

STEP 2
Explaining: *offers some reasons for what they did. These may or may not be correct. The argument may yet not hang together coherently. This is the beginning of inductive reasoning.*

STEP 3
Convincing: *confident that their chain of reasoning is right and may use words such as, 'I reckon' or 'without doubt'. The underlying mathematical argument may or may not be accurate yet is likely to have more coherence and completeness than the explaining stage. This is called inductive reasoning.*

STEP 4
Justifying: *a correct logical argument that has a complete chain of reasoning to it and uses words such as 'because', 'therefore', 'and so', 'that leads to'.*

STEP 5
Proving: *a watertight argument that is mathematically sound, often based on generalisations and underlying structure. This is also called deductive reasoning.*

(NRICH, 2014)

These stages can be useful when teaching reasoning as you can consider where your pupils may currently be in their ability to reason, as well as thinking about where they might need to go next to develop their reasoning further. Whatever stage your pupils are at in terms of their reasoning, building ample opportunities to reason into your lessons is essential if you're going to help your pupils to develop into competent mathematicians who can reason.

Reasoning: key points

- Reasoning is the ability to explain the answer to a given question, to conjecture what would occur in different scenarios, and to spot and describe mathematical patterns. It's one of the three aims for the mathematics National Curriculum and should be a crucial part of pupils' mathematical diet throughout school.

- Informal reasoning, such as asking pupils to regularly explain how they know something or why something is the case, is incredibly important and should occur regularly in every lesson so that pupils know they will always have to explain their thinking.

- More formal reasoning questions should also be used regularly to ensure that pupils have the opportunity to think mathematically in lessons.

- Considering the stages that pupils may pass through as they develop their reasoning is helpful in identifying what pupils could do to improve their reasoning.

20 Depth

The word 'depth' seems to be intrinsically linked to mastery, and the two words are very often used in conjunction. What this word actually means in practice is not easy to pin down though, and the term has become a little amorphous, resulting in commonly-heard platitudes about 'deepening pupils' understanding through mastery' without any clear grasp of what this actually means. In spite of this, we do of course want pupils to deeply understand what they are learning about and to be able to answer a range of complex problems. This chapter will look at what the idea of depth refers to in teaching for mastery and will consider what you can do to promote it in your classroom.

What is depth?

Being able to reason, to solve problems and to work fluently (as described in the National Curriculum) are all important, and considering these three aims will shape the kinds of questions that you include in any activity that you plan. However, our pupils also need to develop their knowledge of the concepts which underpin their ability to answer these questions. When I first started teaching, I would explain a mathematical procedure – columnar addition, for example – and then be satisfied when my pupils were able to use this procedure accurately. I started with easier examples before moving on to more difficult ones, and then finally moved on to larger numbers for my 'top group'. Satisfied that most children had learned to add, I would move on. The pupils had been successful, but it's clear that this didn't represent depth of understanding. These pupils had not had the opportunity to learn in any great depth at all.

There is one important point to mention before trying to define depth, which is that depth is relative, like many of the terms that I've already defined in this book. A pupil who has a deep understanding of addition in Year 1 would not be said to have a deep understanding if they were suddenly placed in Year 5. Depth is about their understanding of what they have learned so far, not the entire maths curriculum. Like the concept of mastery itself, there is no single point where a child has developed 'depth'; it is merely a position on a continuum. Unfortunately, this stands in opposition to what the current teacher assessment frameworks would have us believe, which use the phrase 'greater depth' to refer to a different, higher level of attainment. It is important to note this distinction, as this is not the sense in which I will use the word depth.

It's also important to contrast the idea of depth with acceleration. 'Acceleration' involves moving pupils quickly on to new content when they've initially been successful with a particular learning step or concept. The problem with acceleration is that it doesn't give time to explore a concept further, it doesn't give pupils a chance to consolidate what they're learning and it increases the chance of moving on before all pupils have fully grasped a new concept. For these reasons I'd strongly advocate against the use of acceleration – it's counterproductive to developing clear understanding of the content.

Here is my own definition of what depth refers to in the domain of teaching for mastery. Depth is the ability to answer questions which are not standard in style, which require the application of mathematical thinking as well as mathematical processes, which may require pulling together knowledge of multiple mathematical domains, and which require a clear grasp of the underlying mathematical concepts to solve them successfully.

In short, you could describe depth as the ability to solve complex mathematical problems with an understanding of why a particular method was successful. While this sounds simplistic, I think the discussions around depth have started to give the term a certain mystique which tends to be unhelpful. If we can't define something simply, it will be difficult to plan for it and to understand it. Let's look at an example question and see how it fits with the above definition. This question comes from the NCETM's Year 5 *Teaching for Mastery* assessment booklet.[25]

Using the numbers 3, 4, 5 and 6 only once, make this sum have the smallest possible answer:

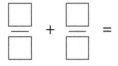

This question isn't a standard fractions question, so pupils may well have not seen this type of question before. It requires knowledge of equivalent fractions and adding fractions, as well as identifying the relative size of fractions. There is a single answer, but there are also multiple different possibilities which are all close in size and not easily comparable. This question also requires mathematical thinking. While it could be solved by identifying each possibility – an important example of mathematical thinking – and then calculating the answer, this would be inefficient.

A much more efficient approach would be to generalise about fractions, for example by realising that any improper fraction – regardless of the numerator or denominator – is always larger than any proper fraction, and then discounting any examples that contain improper fractions. This generalising requires a firm grasp of the concept of fractions. The question also lends itself to adaptation, a hallmark of a well-designed mathematical question. What if it was not an addition calculation but a division instead? How would that change the question? All of these elements combine to make a question which is good for deepening pupils' understanding.

We've repeatedly seen how a key aim of teaching for mastery is to ensure that all pupils become successful mathematicians, and so all activities that you design for your pupils should include questions which aim to deepen their understanding. However, while we may want all pupils to develop deep understanding of the mathematical content that we teach them, we must be aware that, as with all learning, this will happen at different rates for different pupils. The questions that we include in our mathematical activities which are designed to promote deeper understanding might not necessarily be accessed by all pupils in all lessons.

This does not stand in opposition to taking a mastery approach as, crucially, the questions will be available to all pupils; we just know that realistically not all pupils will access them all the time. It's important to remember that questions which can help to deepen pupils' understanding are more difficult than those we would expect the majority of our pupils to access if they had securely grasped the learning in a particular learning step. We should always include these deeper-level questions in our lessons so that our faster-grasping pupils have the opportunity to tackle them, but this will not be every pupil every time. Crucially, what sets such questions apart from the 'challenge activities' that we find in many classrooms is that the questions are securely rooted in the current learning that's being taught, rather than being something picked from later on in the curriculum because it's tricky. Questions that promote depth should take the pupils' current learning but question it in such a way that it requires careful thought to answer.

How to write questions that promote depth

I have defined 'depth' as the ability to answer questions which are not standard in style, which require the application of mathematical thinking as well as mathematical processes, which may require pulling together knowledge of multiple mathematical domains, and which require a clear grasp of the underlying mathematical concepts to solve them successfully. To look at how we can write questions which will promote this ability in our pupils, I want to unpick the constituent elements of my definition:

- *'questions which are not standard in style…'* This means that these questions may appear novel or unusual to learners at first, and if they are problem-solving questions, they may have a fairly opaque surface structure.

- *'… which require the application of mathematical thinking as well as mathematical processes…'* This means that answering such a question will probably not just require a calculation or series of calculations to answer it, but something more too: perhaps pattern-spotting, generalising, systematic working or conjecturing. There may also be multiple possible answers to contend with.

- *'… which may require pulling together knowledge of multiple mathematical domains…'* This means that pupils will need to draw on knowledge from different areas of maths and that the question may not fit neatly into a single domain.

- *'…and which require a clear grasp of the underlying mathematical concepts to solve them successfully'.* This means that pupils can explain why a particular method or plan of attack might work or might be better than another.

Questions that promote depth, then, are likely to contain some of the above elements. Again, this is not a checklist, but a framework for thinking about the questions we give to pupils. When designing an activity, ensure that you plan in some questions that promote depth using some of the elements above. If you are teaching an instructional sequence on addition and subtraction, you could bring in some elements from other mathematical domains, for example ratio and proportion. You could ask a more open question that has multiple possible answers for pupils to identify. You could try to present your question in a different way from usual, so that it requires unpicking, or you could pick a question that has several ways to tackle it. These kinds of choices will ensure your questions promote depth of understanding in your pupils.

There is also the matter of efficiency to consider. The fractions question on page 116 could technically be answered by someone finding all the possible calculations and answering them before comparing every answer, but as we have seen, this would be grossly inefficient. This question could be said to best promote depth when paired with a prompt, perhaps an oral one: 'Do we need to find all the possibilities?', for example. Or: 'What do you know about improper fractions?'. In this way, the depth does not just come from well-designed questions, but also how pupils choose – or are prompted – to answer them.

How can we help pupils to develop depth?

It's clearly important that we provide ample opportunities for depth in our maths lessons. I would suggest that there are three key elements needed for pupils to develop depth of understanding in any given mathematical domain:

- secure foundational knowledge on which the current learning is based
- access to questions which require deeper understanding
- modelled examples of how to solve such questions.

The first point ensures that pupils have the mathematical knowledge needed to actually answer the questions, whilst the latter points make sure that pupils have the opportunity to have a go at such questions and to see an expert mathematician – you – solve them whilst thinking aloud and clearly modelling the relevant thought processes.

Every lesson should have examples of more difficult questions for pupils to answer if they are quick to grasp the core learning of the lesson. In spite of this, the modelling of how to solve these questions need not take place every lesson, as doing so would eat up valuable learning time on a question that not all pupils will attempt. I'd suggest taking an occasional difficult question and modelling how to solve it at the end of a lesson. This means that all pupils are being exposed to such questions from time to time and shown how an expert would answer them. The most important point is that these questions should be a part of the activity in every step of a learning sequence.

Depth: key points

- The idea of deepening pupils' understanding has become intrinsically linked to teaching for mastery.
- Rather than rushing on to new content, more time should be taken to explore each concept in greater depth.
- Questions that help pupils to develop deeper knowledge of maths are varied. However, many share similar features, such as being non-standard, requiring both mathematical thinking – such as pattern spotting, systematic working, conjecturing – and mathematical procedures, crossing mathematical domains and relying on knowledge of the underlying concepts.
- Questions that promote depth will be the most difficult questions that you present your pupils with. Not all pupils will be able to answer these questions, but they should be available to all.
- Including these kinds of questions as part of all learning steps, and sometimes modelling how to solve them, will ensure that pupils become accustomed to seeing them and confident at being able to solve them.

21 Scaffolding

When teaching for mastery, our aim should always be to ensure that all pupils are able to grasp the learning of each learning step before moving on to the next. We've also seen that pupils learn different things at different speeds, and we've explored how intervention can be used to support those who need more time and help to grasp a particular step. Scaffolding is the act of adapting our activities before and during lessons to ensure that as many pupils as possible grasp the learning and so don't need additional intervention after the lesson. Scaffolding refers to any adaptations that we make to our behaviour in lessons or to an activity that pupils will complete in order to support those who need more help.

Similar to interventions, the choices that you make around scaffolding should be rooted in your knowledge of the pupils you teach. You may not always need to scaffold for the same pupils in the same way, and you should make your decisions around scaffolding based on the ongoing and changing needs of your pupils, not simply because of what your pupils have needed in the past. You should have high expectations for all your pupils and your scaffolding should not allow you to lower your expectations of those pupils who require it, but rather it should be used as a means of supporting all your pupils to meet your high expectations.

Scaffolding and differentiation

Scaffolding is obviously a type of differentiation; it involves doing something differently for some pupils and not others. Having said that, scaffolding is a far cry from the kinds of differentiation that I've argued against, where different groups of pupils engage in very different mathematical learning and activities, with teachers effectively running multiple different lessons within one and pupils consequently having varied learning outcomes. Scaffolding is about supporting all pupils so they can grasp the same learning, answer the same questions and ultimately learn the same content. This should be your goal: that all your pupils are supported to learn the entire curriculum. Scaffolding is how we can go about achieving this goal. There are many different ways of scaffolding pupils' learning, but I've chosen three ways to consider here: scaffolding through support, through time and through activity.

Scaffolding through support

Scaffolding through support is probably the easiest way to scaffold, and something that we do naturally as teachers. While pupils are working independently on their activity in a lesson, you will probably be circulating round the classroom, marking as you go and identifying those pupils who are struggling to answer any of the questions. Using your knowledge of the pupils in your class, as well as the evidence of how they are getting on with their work, you can choose to spend additional time with any pupils who require extra support. This can be done individually or in a small group if multiple pupils are having the same problem. If you have additional adults in your classroom, you can instruct them to do the same, but I strongly advise that you work with those pupils who need the most support yourself. As I discussed in Chapter 15 on intervention, the pupils requiring the most support should work with the most knowledgeable and qualified person (the teacher).

While you're working in this way to provide more intensive support to an individual or small group of pupils in your class, it remains important to occasionally circulate around the classroom and see how other pupils are getting on. A significant number of pupils could be struggling with something similar or making errors, and failure to spot this in the lesson can result in a wasted opportunity to address this immediately. So do provide additional support where it's needed, but make sure you also gather information on the rest of the class too. This will avoid any nasty surprises at the end of the lesson.

Scaffolding through time

Scaffolding through time is another way you can give your pupils the support they need to be successful in their learning. As we've seen, different pupils require different amounts of time to learn new material, and some pupils are also slower at working through a set of questions. Scaffolding through time involves ensuring that those pupils who need additional time to complete an activity are given it. This may simply involve sending work home to be completed, finding more time for them during the day (perhaps during registration time), or having them attend a keep-up intervention to complete the work.

Giving sufficient time to those who need it is a crucial element of mastery. Sometimes, pupils won't be able to finish the activity you've designed for them because some of the later questions are more difficult than earlier ones. If this is the case, you should make a decision as to whether they have sufficiently grasped the learning or not, which will inform whether or not they should attend a keep-up intervention. Remember, not all pupils will always be able to answer the most difficult questions that you set (even if this is your ideal aim), but you must decide whether pupils know enough to be able to move on to the next lesson and be successful in that.

Scaffolding through activity

Scaffolding through activity is the third form of scaffolding that we'll look at. The most time-consuming type, perhaps, but also very powerful. Scaffolding through activity involves making adaptations to the work that pupils complete, either before or during the lesson. These changes will vary based upon the needs of your pupils, but crucially they don't involve changing the actual questions that pupils will answer. Some ideas of the different ways you can scaffold an activity are suggested below.

- **Providing additional worked examples.** You'll have used worked examples at some point in your teaching during a learning step, either on the board or in books. Beginning a set of questions with a worked example will provide useful support for your pupils if they need it.

- **Partially completing some problems.** This is useful where pupils may not have fully grasped the steps in a procedure. Partially completing some problems gives pupils a guide for what to do – similar to a completion problem, except that pupils have had only some of the work done for them in one or two examples.

- **Including representations.** Including visual representations of the numbers and processes involved in answering a question can be a useful scaffold, serving as a reminder for pupils. For example, a visual representation such as a bar model of $\frac{2}{7}$ and $\frac{3}{7}$ may help pupils to remember why you don't add denominators when adding fractions (see Figure 21).

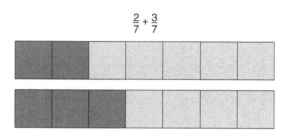

Figure 21

- Likewise, a partially partitioned array may help pupils to remember which numbers they must multiply in long division. These additional representations can either be added to an activity before the lesson if you know they're likely to be needed, or created impromptu in the lesson should the need arise.

- **Providing additional resources.** For some pupils, additional physical resources and manipulatives can give them the support they need to answer questions. However, there are a couple of things to bear in mind when considering providing this kind of scaffolding for pupils. Firstly, pupils shouldn't become reliant upon concrete resources. The primary purpose of concrete resources isn't to help pupils to answer calculations, but to help them to see the mathematical structures present. The aim is *always* for pupils to be able to answer questions in the abstract, not to rely on concrete resources when calculating. For this reason, I suggest that these resources are used sparingly in order to support pupils with answering questions.

  Secondly, it's important to remember that concrete resources should be used with all pupils, not just pupils who require additional support, so aim to use concrete resources as part of the normal teaching process, rather than only with pupils who seem stuck or need help.

These methods of scaffolding will ensure that the high expectations you set for your pupils can be met by as many of them as possible without the need for additional intervention.

Scaffolding

Scaffolding: key points

- Scaffolding refers to the ways, both before and during lessons, that you can support all of your pupils to grasp the point of a lesson. It's a form of differentiation, but the point is to get every pupil to access the same learning.

- Scaffolding can mitigate the need for additional intervention after the lesson, maximising the number of pupils who are initially successful in grasping the learning.

- Scaffolding can be provided through support, by spending time with pupils during the lesson to aid them in their work.

- Scaffolding can be provided through time, by allowing pupils extra time to complete their work.

- Scaffolding can be provided through adapting the activities that pupils complete. This is done by providing additional support rather than changing the questions that pupils must answer.

22 Delivering an activity

We've looked at the constituent elements of an activity that you might ask pupils to complete as part of a lesson or learning step. Let's now consider how to pull these elements together into an activity that will allow pupils to practise and learn the mathematical content of each learning step. We know that most activities should have a mixture of fluency, reasoning and problem solving questions, although this doesn't need to be the case in every single activity. As I previously described, a higher proportion of questions aimed at developing fluency may be appropriate earlier on in an instructional sequence, while the proportion of problem-solving activities may increase later, but all three elements should be present throughout an instructional sequence.

Questions of the same sort don't necessarily need to be grouped together in an activity, so there is no problem in mixing up question types. Bearing in mind that pupils need to practise not only new learning but also prior learning, it's important to include questions from previous learning steps and previous instructional sequences from time to time. Mixing these in with your new learning questions will ensure that pupils are regularly having to think about and practise their prior learning.

Something that I recommend strongly is using progressive questioning. Progressive questions are simply questions that get incrementally more difficult as they go along. This is common practice: most assessments start with easier questions and leave the hardest ones to the end. Planning your activities in this way is very useful as it allows all pupils to get started with an easier question or two before the difficulty increases. It also means that you can gather information on how your pupils are getting on with their learning by seeing what they find difficult.

Designing questions so that they get progressively more difficult takes some practice, as it's sometimes hard to work out which questions pupils will find harder – indeed, it often depends on the pupils. Having said this, it's a powerful way of making sure your pupils are all able to access the activity independently through having a low threshold to start with before ramping up the difficulty. Remember that each activity you design should have questions (probably towards the end) that are your 'deepening understanding' questions. These questions will be those meaty, non-standard questions described in Chapter 20 on depth.

It's important that you work through and answer any questions yourself before you give them to your pupils (even if you already have the answers available to you). Going through this process allows you to see the questions from the point of view of your pupils, which helps in the process of anticipating and understanding their errors and misconceptions. This in turn will help you to notice and correct these errors more swiftly. I mentioned using a tracker earlier in the book – a sheet to gather data on your pupils' performance in a lesson. My tracker is always simply a copy of the pupils' activity that I've completed myself before the lesson starts. I can then refer to this when circulating during the lesson and use it to note down questions that are proving particularly problematic by means of a simple tally.

Each learning step that you plan should have an activity, and the activity should indicate whether your pupils are ready to move on to the next learning step. We can think of the activity as the gate that our pupils walk through to get to the next learning step. The activity that you design for a particular learning step helps to guide you in your teaching, prompting you to think about what you'll need to teach your pupils to enable them to successfully complete the questions contained in your activity. While you want to be sure that you get a high degree of success from your pupils, it's important to bear in mind that not all pupils will be able to access the most difficult questions aimed at deepening their understanding, but this does not mean they've failed to grasp the core learning of the step.

Delivering an activity: key points

- The vast majority of activities that you design should contain elements of fluency, reasoning and problem solving, although the question types can be mixed up.

- It's a good idea to include some questions from previous learning steps and instructional sequences to provide another element of review.

- Progressive questioning (steadily increasing the difficulty of questions) is useful to ensure that all pupils can access the initial questions independently, and then work through questions of increasing difficulty.

- Questions aimed at deepening pupils' understanding should be included in every activity – probably towards the end, as they'll be among the most difficult questions that we ask our pupils to answer.

- Answering the questions that you pose pupils yourself gives you a useful insight into any difficulties they may come up against.

PART 3

Leading for mastery

A look at how you can implement a mastery approach school-wide, considering leadership, culture and training

23 Becoming a maths lead

This chapter is aimed at those who are new to the position of a primary school mathematics lead, or who might be considering it in the near future. The role is an absolutely excellent one, and leading mathematics has been, and remains, one of my favourite aspects of working in primary schools. I will draw on my own experience, as well as that of colleagues in similar roles, to give some advice on taking on the role. However, it's important to note here that context is key. Schools vary enormously and have wildly different levels of existing mathematics provision, staff experience and access to resources. Crucially, schools are all at different stages on their journeys and this requires you to act accordingly.

My first mathematics lead role was in a 'failing' school with a very high staff turnover and poor results, which had been given notice to close by the local authority. The new teachers who started at the same time as me were relatively young and inexperienced, and I was new to the role and the school. Needless to say, the way in which I approached leading maths in this school is very different to how I would lead it in a stable, successful school with a knowledgeable and experienced staff. Context is king. Having said that, there are many elements that would need tackling in both of these schools, but they may need to be approached in different ways.

When I first started teaching, despite the training that I'd received, I knew next to nothing about teaching mathematics. Unfortunately, thanks to the Dunning-Kruger effect, I also had no idea of this. The Dunning-Kruger effect describes that fact that those with low ability in a particular area often over estimate their ability in that area. Their lack of knowledge makes it difficult for them to evaluate their level of knowledge. As Shakespeare said, 'The fool doth think he is wise, but the wise man knows himself to be a fool.'[26] Or in other words, you don't know what you don't know. I knew that I could do the maths required at primary-school level, in terms of solving problems and answering questions, and I naively thought this would be enough to teach my pupils what they needed to know. Luckily, once I started teaching I was soon divested of this notion, and had the opportunity to work with many experienced colleagues who helped me to develop my knowledge and craft.

Teaching pupils well requires a wealth of knowledge about mathematics, far beyond the ability to 'do the work'. As I mentioned earlier in the book, this fact is something of a paradox: teaching any subject well requires a strong base of domain-specific knowledge, and yet primary schools are set up to favour generalist teachers. I firmly believe it's possible to develop the level of subject knowledge required to consider yourself a 'specialist' at primary level and thus deliver consistently excellent teaching, but it requires both time and effort. Your job as a leader is to facilitate this increase in subject knowledge, first for yourself and then for your teachers. The latter will be addressed in the next chapter on CPD, but for now let's look at the former.

When I first became a maths lead, I was working with a relatively new and inexperienced team. While I had a few years' more knowledge and experience than most of the teachers, I was very aware that I had an awful lot to learn: I had never led mathematics before nor worked in a 'challenging' school. I made increasing my own subject knowledge a priority. My headteacher at the time encouraged all the teachers to complete the NCETM's self-evaluation tools, which I did.[27] I'd strongly recommend this for all teachers, whether leading mathematics or not. This tool enabled me to recognise some of the gaps in my own subject knowledge, which I could then work on improving.

I began to work on improving my subject knowledge in two ways: through reading and through attending training. The book that I initially found to be most helpful was Derek Haylock's *Mathematics Explained for Primary Teachers*.[28] This book, a required text on many teacher training courses, provides a useful, quick reference guide to the areas of mathematics covered in the National Curriculum. It gave me a valuable starting point to plug some of the gaps in my own knowledge. There are a number of other books that I read at the time and found particularly useful, including Mike Askew's *Transforming Primary Mathematics*.[29] Today I'd also firmly recommend the following to those new to subject leadership, as they have shaped my thinking a lot recently:

- Craig Barton's *How I Wish I'd Taught Maths*[30]
- Ed Southall's *Yes, But Why?*[31]
- Peter Mattock's *Visible Maths*[32]

In addition to all of the excellent books available, there are a number of education bloggers who bring their expertise and wisdom to some of the biggest questions and debates within education today. I highly recommend reading around the reflections of bloggers who work in schools day to day. I've learned an incredible amount from blogs, and even reading things that I've disagreed with profoundly have helped to shape my thoughts and ideas around education. Some of the most interesting mathematical blogs that I've read include the following:

- Craig Barton: www.mrbartonmaths.com/blog
- Mark McCourt: www.emaths.co.uk
- Kris Boulton: https://tothereal.wordpress.com
- Hin-Tai Ting: https://mathagogy.wordpress.com
- Ed Southall: https://solvemymaths.com

Aside from reading to increase my subject knowledge, I was also lucky enough to attend a series of excellent courses in the early stages of my career. Being able to learn from real experts in the field of mathematics education can really take your understanding to another level. I'd suggest looking to your local maths hubs as a starting point for this, as well as other mathematical organisations who work to support teachers. There are a number of subject associations that support maths teachers, but two of them provide information and support specific to primary schools: the Mathematical Association (MA) and the Association of Teachers of Mathematics (ATM). I wish that I'd known about their existence earlier in my career, because they provide excellent training, journals and books, and their entire raison d'être is improving the quality of teaching in mathematics. Membership of both these organisations is worth every penny, and I can't recommend it enough.

The subject associations also run mathematics conferences (as do other organisations such as Mathematics Mastery and La Salle Education). These are a wonderful way of developing your own subject knowledge, and the diversity of speakers at such events means that you'll almost always discover something unexpected and interesting. Attending these conferences, meeting other maths teachers and listening to speakers discuss a wide variety of topics all pertinent to mathematics education can be a powerful experience. Some of the best training I've experienced has been at conferences, often after having gone without the intention of learning about anything in particular.

I should also mention a place that has allowed me to find so many of the books, blogs, conferences and training opportunities that I've mentioned above: Twitter. I'm not an avowed Twitterphile by any means, but there's a huge amount that I've learned from Twitter, both directly and indirectly, that feeds into conversations with colleagues about how to teach maths, and I have no doubt that I would be a poorer teacher and leader without the influence of Twitter. In the 'Additional Reading' section at the end of this book, I list some of my favourite Twitter accounts to follow. I hope they help to develop your thinking as much as they helped to develop mine.

As well as developing your subject knowledge and expanding your thinking around the subject of mathematics, the other main piece of advice that I can give to new subject leads is to try to visit other schools that have a well-established way of teaching mathematics successfully. Speak to teachers and leaders (especially the maths lead) and find out what systems there are in place to ensure that maths teaching runs smoothly there. I was lucky enough to do this as a visitor earlier in my career and as a host more recently. It's a very interesting thing to do and can really help you to think through some of the questions you might have about how you can ensure that maths is taught as effectively as possible in your own school. Learning from the successes and errors of others is a worthwhile way of spending your time, and while it won't answer all of your questions, it will certainly make you think.

Becoming a maths lead: key points

- A key element of leadership is being able to walk the walk: make sure you are as good a mathematics teacher as possible if you are going to lead the subject.

- Good subject knowledge is a must. Read around the subject, go to watch and speak to the best teachers that you can, attend training and continually strive to improve yourself as a teacher and leader.

- Join one (or more) of the subject associations – they have a wealth of expertise and knowledge and are an excellent way to make additional contacts.

- Attend conferences – you never know who you'll meet and what you'll learn.

- Use Twitter – the benefits of what's available to be learned there far outweigh the annoyances.

- Visit schools who are teaching maths successfully and find out how they are doing this. Not everything will work for you and your school, but some ideas will be incredibly useful.

24 CPD

The Sutton Trust report *What Makes Great Teaching?* is emphatically clear on the answer to the question that its title poses: teachers' (pedagogical) content knowledge and quality of instruction.[33] Both of these factors have a huge effect on the quality of education that our pupils receive. I firmly believe that the general training which trainee primary teachers in England receive doesn't equip us with the depth of knowledge needed to teach the subject effectively, especially as the routes into the profession are so fragmented. I therefore believe that no matter the experience, age or make-up of your staff, it's the duty of a maths lead in a primary school to run regular sessions of CPD for teachers. This is the focus of this chapter.

In the previous chapter, I talked about the external CPD that I was able to attend in the early days of leading mathematics, which made such a big difference to my professional knowledge and practice. External CPD certainly has its place, but it has some clear limitations. Firstly, it's unlikely that any school, especially in the current climate, has the budget to send all of its teachers on external training, or has the capacity to facilitate the cover necessary for this.

Equally, it's possible to buy in support from external experts who can train all the staff in your school. This has the benefit of involving all the teachers in a school, but it's also by its very nature transitory. Such people come for a day, deliver their training and are then gone again. I don't wish to suggest that sending teachers on external courses or buying in experts shouldn't be done; I've used both of these techniques as a maths lead. However, these approaches won't address the need for high-quality training that exists in most primary schools. They can only ever supplement something else: systematic CPD for all teachers, delivered using the expertise that exists within the school. I firmly believe this is the only sustainable way to consistently drive forward improvements in the maths teaching that a school provides.

The first stage in setting up such a system is to ensure that you, or others within your school, have the knowledge to be able to start training your teachers. Once you've had the opportunity to start developing your own subject knowledge, you must start looking at how to share this knowledge with your staff. I suggest considering two linked, but distinct, types of training that it is likely you'll want to run:

- training to develop teachers' pedagogical content knowledge
- training to implement or develop systems and procedures to organise how maths is taught.

Let's now look at how to structure training in each of these areas in turn.

CPD in pedagogical content knowledge

As discussed earlier in Chapter 3, pedagogical content knowledge sits at the nexus of subject knowledge and pedagogy – it involves knowing the mathematics and knowing how best to teach it.

I would suggest organising this type of CPD by splitting the mathematical content along the lines of the National Curriculum. The primary maths curriculum is divided into the following strands:

- Number and place value
- Addition and subtraction
- Multiplication and division
- Fractions, including decimals and percentages
- Ratio and proportion
- Algebra
- Measurement
- Geometry: properties of shape
- Geometry: position and direction
- Statistics

The names of the strands aren't consistent in each year group; the four operations, for example, are grouped into a single strand in the Year 6 programme of study. However, knowledge of all these strands is essential to good teaching, and together the strands cover a wide range of mathematical knowledge, from early counting to the beginnings of algebra. I know of a number of schools that split their CPD into key stage- or year group-specific sessions, but I think it's a mistake to do this as a matter of course. Aside from the fact that all teachers should be able to teach the full gamut of primary school mathematics if required, even a teacher who only ever teaches a single year group needs to know the full extent of the curriculum. Firstly, this is because different groups of pupils will be at different stages in their mathematical development. They'll have different prior knowledge and will thus require different starting points. As discussed earlier, what to teach should not be mandated by the age of the pupils but by their existing knowledge, and teachers need to know where this knowledge sits.

Secondly, it's important that teachers have an appreciation of both where the pupils have come from and where they are heading, in terms of their mathematical learning. Coherence is a crucial element of maths and knowing where the content that you're trying to teach sits within a broader journey is essential. Teachers need to understand the big ideas in maths, the repeating themes and motifs that pupils will encounter time and time again in their learning, and they need to be able to link what they're teaching now to what has previously been learned, or what will be learned in the future. For these reasons, I strongly recommend running the same CPD for all your teachers, to give all of them the knowledge needed to teach effectively.

In terms of structuring CPD on pedagogical content knowledge, I think it's best to take each curriculum strand separately at first and design a CPD session based on that strand alone. This allows you to focus on the mathematical learning within that particular domain. In delivering CPD strand by strand there is a risk, however. The risk is that teachers – and by extension, their pupils – will come to consider these strands as separate and distinct from one another. The strands are organised like this in the National Curriculum for convenience. In reality, the strands are linked, interwoven and often inseparable from each other. How can we consider addition to be distinct from multiplication, for example, when an understanding of the former provides the initial learning of the latter?

Mathematics is a complex, interwoven body of knowledge, much more akin to a web than a series of separate strands. Demonstrating links between different strands of the curriculum is therefore important. The explicit sharing of mathematical big ideas helps to identify commonalities between the strands, which is why I also recommend running CPD on some of the key mathematical ideas, considering how they appear and resurface across the curriculum.

When designing CPD on a mathematical strand, I think it's important to capture the following elements:

- **Progression.** It's important for teachers to be able to clearly understand the progression of learning steps within a particular strand. Because of the hierarchical nature of maths learning, the order in which things are taught is crucial. Teachers must be able to see how the learning in a particular area builds up over time. While this can start with the National Curriculum statements within a particular strand, it's necessary to go beyond this as these statements are incredibly broad. Breaking down these statements into smaller steps and then sequencing them effectively is a crucial starting point to building a school's curriculum.

- **Misconceptions.** A key element of pedagogical content knowledge is knowledge of misconceptions. Any CPD on a particular area of maths should include some of the most frequently encountered misconceptions to enable teachers to recognise, plan for and respond to them.

- **Exemplar questions.** Designing questions is one of the most difficult things to do for a novice teacher. Including high-quality question examples in CPD sessions ensures that teachers are exposed to a range of high-quality questions that pupils could be asked to tackle within a mathematical domain.

- **Representations.** The way that we represent mathematical ideas and concepts is central to how our pupils will learn mathematics. Take the opportunity in CPD sessions to share some of the key representations for that domain of mathematics.

- **Big ideas.** These concepts that recur across many different areas of maths should be addressed in domain-specific CPD, helping teachers to see links between different domains.

Including these elements in your CPD will give your teachers a clear overview of the key learning within each strand, give them a clear understanding of the learning journey that pupils will experience and provide them with the beginnings of how to plan within each strand. It will also ensure that the links between each strand are explained and explored.

CPD in systems and procedures

The second type of CPD to consider delivering are sessions regarding systems and methods of teaching mathematics. These sessions are designed to consider how mathematics is organised in your school, what maths lessons look like, and what school-wide systems and procedures are in place. The frequency and content of such sessions will depend greatly on your school and factors such as staff experience, turnover and how well-embedded practice is. With newer members of staff, or when making changes to the way that maths is taught, it's important to include these more operational sessions in your CPD. It is also a useful thing to do from time to time as a reminder of the norms and expectations in your school's maths lessons.

I'm inherently wary of prescribing in detail how teachers should teach in their classrooms – far better to establish a set of shared principles about what good teaching looks like, as this understanding will guide the actions of teachers when designing lessons. One of the main reasons for this is that any one-size-fits-all approach will not work, as some lessons and learning steps have to deviate from others in order to be effective. Having said that, I do believe there are times when certain things should be mandated. Review, for example, is so important that it must play a part in the vast majority of maths lessons. The decision of what to mandate and what to leave to teachers' judgement is not easy, will depend on a number of factors and may well change over time. However, what must underpin any approach is a strong culture of professionalism, an understanding of the purpose of maths education, and a shared appreciation of what good maths teaching looks like.

Delivering CPD

Having considered the two types of CPD that it's important to run, it's worth taking a minute to consider logistics. I'm sure that you have, up to this point, been thinking about the key limiting factor in schools: time. The CPD described in this chapter would require a great deal of dedicated time to deliver. Running a single CPD session for each of the ten curriculum strands, plus a couple of sessions for systems and organisation, amounts to twelve sessions, or two per half term. This is roughly one third of staff meetings that a school might have over the course of an academic year. This is difficult in a primary school with so many competing interests.

Firstly, I would say that maths is a core subject and an essential element of a good primary education, so it should have a high priority when it comes to allocating staff meeting time. Secondly, I think it's common for schools to use staff meeting time for operational elements such as discussing upcoming events and giving notices, and I'd suggest that this time is far better spent focusing on teaching and learning. Operations can often be covered in staff briefings or via email. Thirdly, I'd suggest that it's possible to find more time for staff CPD.

For example, I've worked with a number of schools that have decided to implement two shorter staff meetings per week to enable them to fit in more CPD. Teachers typically find these CPD sessions very useful, and this focus on teaching and learning often becomes a key part of the school's culture. However you do it, fight for as much CPD time as you can, and make good use of it. If you can't have as much time as you would like (and who ever does, really?), ensure that you provide your teachers with high-quality support materials and that you're readily available to have discussions with your colleagues about mathematics – something that is often the most enjoyable part of my day.

A note on practice

Practising anything is the key to both learning it initially and then improving it later. However, we often don't give our teachers the time in CPD sessions to deliberately practise what we're asking them to implement in their classrooms. The problem with this is that in the reality of day-to-day teaching, messages and ideas can get lost, forgotten and misinterpreted. Deliberate practice, in a setting where this is the main focus – i.e. a CPD session – allows teachers to concentrate on one thing and one thing only. It also allows you to focus on giving feedback on what teachers are doing. I strongly advocate building time into your CPD sessions for practice. This practice could involve writing example questions, breaking down learning into smaller steps, or modelling a worked example or the use of a particular manipulative. The excellent book *Practice Perfect* makes fascinating further reading on this topic.[34]

CPD: key points

- Typically, primary teachers don't enter the profession with the pedagogical content knowledge needed to teach maths effectively.

- All schools should deliver a coherent programme of regular CPD to all their teachers to improve the quality of teaching across the board.

- External training and consultants can supplement the CPD needs of a school, but they can't meet the entire CPD needs of a school.

- There are two distinct types of CPD that you may want to deliver: training on pedagogical content knowledge in maths and training on systems and organisation.

- Pedagogical content knowledge CPD can be organised using the National Curriculum strands as a starting point, considering progression, misconceptions, questions, representations and big ideas.

- Systems and organisation CPD includes anything that is non-subject knowledge-based which helps teachers to consider how maths is taught. The profile of your school will determine the necessity of such sessions and their content.

- CPD should provide teachers with the opportunity to put into practice what is being covered in the sessions.

25 School culture

This chapter, the last in the book, could easily have been the first. Setting up the right culture is absolutely crucial to the success of maths teaching in your school, and this falls partly on the shoulders of whoever is leading that area. Obviously there's an element of shared responsibility and the school's senior team will also have a role in driving this, but if you're the maths lead then you are the subject's main defender, promoter and champion. You may have multiple roles and responsibilities, especially if you work in a smaller school, but the subject leadership of maths is an absolutely pivotal role and you should have regular time devoted to this task. Part of this time should be used to deliberately build up the culture that will support the success of maths teaching in your school.

In the UK and the US (our cultural cousin), maths doesn't have the reputation that it deserves. People will attest to being poor mathematicians, sometimes boasting about this as if it's something to be proud of. This perhaps comes from a place of self-preservation and serves to deflect embarrassment, but there is no parallel in terms of literacy; save for a very small and unusual minority, people aren't proud of being illiterate and don't proclaim themselves to 'not be an English person'. The reasons for this are complex and difficult to pin down, but something that feeds people's perception of the subject is surely down to the portrayal of maths in the media. The video *Hollywood Hates Math,* which I first saw during some training run by the organisation Mathematics Mastery, is a shocking revelation of how often maths is denigrated in film and television.[35] The message is there, loud and clear: maths is unimportant, difficult and boring; it's not worth trying to be good at; people who do like maths are uncool, unlikeable nerds. Whatever the reasons, few would argue with the fact that our society abounds with negative images and messages about maths, and our pupils are bombarded with these messages, both implicitly and explicitly.

This negativity may be common in the world at large, but it's our job to ensure that it never crosses the threshold of our schools. Everything that we do in school must counteract the negativity around maths that pupils will face elsewhere. School must be a place of relentless positivity when it comes to maths. It is beautiful, it is useful, it is important. People who are good at maths are intelligent and valued. These messages must come both explicitly and implicitly from everyone in the school, from the headteacher down.

I think that people's attitudes towards maths are worth addressing during CPD, perhaps during an INSET day when all teachers and support staff are present, as the consistency of this message is so important. In any school, there will be people who have negative feelings towards maths. The reasons for this vary: perhaps they were badly taught, or they received unhelpful messages from their parents and teachers. However, these feelings must not be shared or passed on to pupils. Every adult in school should appear to love maths in front of the pupils. Whether this love is real (the ideal situation) or is feigned by some (more likely), it must be present, nonetheless.

Implicit messages are just as important as explicit ones. Saying *'make sure you behave or you'll have to stay in at break and do some maths'* (something I've heard said in a school) will not do; we want to build a culture where this would be a reward and not a sanction. I'm not personally an advocate for 'maths weeks' or similar tokenistic attempts to push the prominence of the subject. Every week should be maths week and giving it an artificial prominence for one week will only serve to diminish its prominence for the other 38 weeks of the school year. Maths should be important all year round.

How do we go about building this culture? Well, in the same way that the messages adults give to pupils must be considered carefully, so must be the messages that we as school leaders give to our staff. We must signal that maths is one of the most crucial things that we teach in primary school (second only to teaching our pupils how to read, in my opinion) and that it must be given precedence. It should be taught every day, for at least an hour, and should be the last thing to go when timetables need to be changed. We must encourage all our staff (both teachers and teaching assistants) to develop their subject knowledge and expertise in maths, and we must support this process. This will come about partly through the CPD that we provide, but we must also encourage a culture of scholarship amongst our staff, so that everyone takes responsibility for the development of their own knowledge.

School culture: key points

- A school's culture and overall approach towards maths underpins the learning that takes place in the school.

- Western culture frequently undervalues the role of maths and of mathematicians. The messages about maths in the media, both implicit and explicit, are overwhelmingly negative ones.

- Schools must be a place of relentless positivity about maths, and this message must come from each and every member of staff consistently.

- This culture is set from the top and requires school leaders to explicitly explain and implicitly demonstrate the importance and inherent value of mathematics as a discipline.

Conclusion

Teaching for mastery has been a hotly contested topic in recent years, with some schools using approaches under the label 'mastery' that are actually anything but. I hope this book has brought you some clarity as to what teaching for mastery is, and provided enough practical advice for you to start implementing the approach in your classroom or school. Mastery is not a quick fix. It's not possible to suddenly switch to a mastery approach when teachers have been used to teaching differently, and pupils may have large gaps in attainment within a single year group. However, with careful planning and commitment, it's possible for schools to effectively implement teaching for mastery and to ensure that all pupils have the opportunity to become successful mathematicians.

The key elements of teaching for mastery that have been covered in this book are all important individually, but it's combining them into a coherent approach that makes them so powerful. For this reason, I'd suggest that you don't simply pick and choose the elements of the approach that you like the sound of but take the time to implement the whole approach. It does take time, hard work and careful management, but what worthwhile endeavour doesn't? The time spent on delivering your own high-quality CPD, for instance, will pay dividends in increasing staff retention and in empowering teachers to be the experts in the classroom. The carefully planned lessons will ensure that as many pupils as possible are able to access the learning, and quick, effective intervention will be there for pupils who do not. The approach is well worth the effort.

Everyone has the potential to be a successful mathematician. Everyone can learn mathematics. A secure foundation in mathematics is the right of every child who goes through the education system, and teaching for mastery is the best means by which this potential can begin to become a reality. I hope that the advice in this book will bring you and your colleagues closer to creating this reality for all the pupils that you teach.

Additional reading

This is a list of wider reading, including books, websites and Twitter accounts to follow. Some have been mentioned over the course of this book, while others have not. While the collection is perhaps a little eclectic, what they all have in common is that they have helped to improve me as a maths educator in some way.

Books

Memorable Teaching – Peps Mccrea

> A short, clear book outlining how we can make sure our pupils remember what we teach them.

Teach Like a Champion 2.0. – Doug Lemov

> While not strictly mathematical, the vast majority of the techniques in this seminal pedagogical text apply to the teaching of mathematics.

Thinking Mathematically – John Mason with Leone Burton and Kaye Stacey

> A book full of fascinating problems that explains with absolute clarity how we think when engaging in mathematics.

Mathematics Explained for Primary Teachers – Derek Haylock and Ralph Manning

> *The* book to buy to improve your pedagogical content knowledge in maths.

Transforming Primary Mathematics – Mike Askew

> A book that made me think differently about what maths is and what it is for.

How I Wish I'd Taught Maths – Craig Barton

> A forensically written book, outlining some of the common mistakes in mathematics teaching and how to avoid them. A great source of research too.

Yes, But Why? Teaching for Understanding in Mathematics – Ed Southall

> A book explaining some of the opaque concepts in maths – great for pedagogy and subject knowledge too.

Visible Maths – Peter Mattock

> A beautiful book on mathematical representations and how teachers can use them to make maths 'visible'.

Tackling Misconceptions in Primary Mathematics – Kieran Mackle

> A book which clearly identifies some of the key misconceptions that primary school pupils may have in mathematics.

Websites

https://www.ncetm.org.uk

A wide variety of articles and resources, including progression maps, mastery assessment booklets, professional development materials and more.

https://mathsbot.com

Superb website with a range of digital manipulatives and much more. Really useful for modelling on an interactive whiteboard.

https://www.mathsisfun.com

A one-stop shop for clear mathematical definitions and explanations.

https://nrich.maths.org

An excellent bank of rich mathematical tasks and articles.

https://ssddproblems.com

A collection of problem sets which have the same surface but different deep structures to get pupils looking beyond a question's context when practising problem solving.

Twitter accounts

Bernie Westacott: @berniewestacott
Dani Quinn: @danicquinn
Susan Okereke: @dothemathsthing
Lisa: @elsie2110
Mark McCourt: @emathsuk
Greg Ashman: @greg_ashman
Jemma Sherwood: @jemmaths
Kate Milnes: @katban70
Kristopher Boulton: @kris_boulton
Jo Morgan: @mathsjem
Ben Gordon: @mathsmrgordon
Mattematics: @mattswain36
Emma McCrea: @mccreaemma
Craig Barton: @mrbartonmaths
Peter Mattock: @mrmattock
Naveen Rizvi: @naveenfrizvi
Solomon Kingsnorth: @solomon_teach
Christopher Such: @suchmo83
Mike Thain: @thainmike

References

1   Kingsnorth, S. (2018). *Year 1: differentiate 3 ways please; Year 2: differentiate 3 ways please; Year 3: differentiate 3 ways please; Year 4: differentiate 3 ways please; Year 5: differentiate 3 ways please; Year 6: make them all pass the same test please* (Twitter). 19 September. Available at: https://twitter.com/solomon_teach/status/1042509055242190849?s=20 (Accessed 2 August 2019).

2   Rosenthal, R., and Jacobson, L. (1966). 'Teachers' Expectancies: Determinants of Pupils' IQ Gains', *Psychological Reports*, 19/1, 115–118.

3   Rosenshine, B. (2012). 'Principles of Instruction: Research-Based Strategies That All Teachers Should Know', *American Educator*, Spring 2012, 12–39.

4   Coe R., Aloisi C., Higgins S., and Major, L. E. (2014). *What Makes Great Teaching? Review of the Underpinning Research* (London: The Sutton Trust).

5   Gersten, R., Jordan, N. C., and Flojo, J. R. (2005). 'Early Identification and Interventions for Students with Mathematics Difficulties', *Journal of Learning Disabilities*, 38/4, 293–304.

6   Kirschner, P. A., Sweller, J., and Clark, R. E. (2006). 'Why Minimal Guidance During Instruction Does Not Work: An Analysis of the Failure of Constructivist, Discovery, Problem-Based, Experiential, and Inquiry-Based Teaching', *Educational Psychologist*, 41/2, 75–86.

7   Didau, D. (2019). *Making Kids Cleverer* (Carmarthen: Crown House Publishing).

8   Kirschner, P. A., Sweller, J., and Clark, R. E. (2006). 'Why Minimal Guidance During Instruction Does Not Work: An Analysis of the Failure of Constructivist, Discovery, Problem-Based, Experiential, and Inquiry-Based Teaching', *Educational Psychologist*, 41/2, 75–86.

9   Ashman, G. (2016). 'Six Tips to Improve Your Explicit Teaching', *Filling the Pail*. 15 July. Available at: https://gregashman.wordpress.com/2016/07/15/six-tips-to-improve-your-explicit-teaching (Accessed 2 August 2019).

10 Charles, R. (2005). 'Big Ideas and Understandings as the Foundation for Elementary and Middle School Mathematics', *NCSM Journal of Mathematics Education Leadership*, 8/1., 9–24.

11 Askew, M. (2015). *Big Ideas in Mathematics Education: Teaching for Deep Understanding* (Oxford: Oxford University Press).

12 Morgan, D. (2012). 'Five Big Ideas', *Mathematics Teaching*, 227, 49–50.

13 Barclay, N., and Barnes, A. (2013). 'Big Ideas – An Idea With Primary Potential?', *Mathematics Teaching*, 234, 19–21.

14 Mccrea, P. (2017) *Memorable Teaching* (CreateSpace).

15 Murre, J. M. J., and Dros, J. (2015). 'Replication and Analysis of Ebbinghaus' Forgetting Curve', *PLoS ONE*, 10/7.

16 Rosenshine, B. (2012). 'Principles of Instruction: Research-Based Strategies That All Teachers Should Know', *American Educator*, Spring 2012, 12–39.

17 Marton, F. (2012). 'Foreword' in Lo, M. L. (2012) *Variation Theory and the Improvement of Teaching and Learning* (Sweden: Acta Universitatis Gothoburgensis).

18 Lemov, D. (2015). *Teach Like a Champion 2.0.* (2nd edn, San Francisco: Jossey Bass).

19 Department for Education (2014). *National Curriculum in England: Mathematics Programmes of Study.* Available at: https://www.gov.uk/government/publications/national-curriculum-in-england-

mathematics-programmes-of-study/national-curriculum-in-england-mathematics-programmes-of-study (Accessed 2 August 2019).

20   Russell, S. J. (2000). 'Developing Computational Fluency with Whole Numbers in the Elementary Grades', *New England Mathematics Journal*, 32/2, 40–54.

21   National Centre for Excellence in the Teaching of Mathematics, *National Curriculum – Reasoning and Problem Solving: Key Stage 2: Mathematics Content Knowledge, Question 1(e)*. Available at: https://www.ncetm.org.uk/self-evaluation/browse/strand/5238 (Accessed 2 August 2019).

22   Mason, J., Burton, L. and Stacey, K. (2010). *Thinking Mathematically* (2nd edn, Pearson).

23   National Centre for Excellence in the Teaching of Mathematics (2014). *Achieving the Aims of the New National Curriculum: Developing Opportunities and Ensuring Progression in the Development of Reasoning Skills*. Available at: https://www.ncetm.org.uk/resources/44672 (Accessed 2 August 2019).

24   NRICH Primary Team (2014). *Reasoning: the Journey from Novice to Expert*. (Cambridge: Cambridge University Press).

25   National Centre for Excellence in the Teaching of Mathematics (2015). *Teaching for Mastery: Questions, Tasks and Activities to Support Assessment – Year 5*. (Oxford: Oxford University Press).

26   Shakespeare, W. (2002). *The Complete Pelican Shakespeare*. Orgel, S. and Braunmuller, A. R. (eds). (New York: Penguin Books).

27   National Centre for Excellence in the Teaching of Mathematics, *Mathematics Teaching Self-evaluation Tools*. Available at: https://www.ncetm.org.uk/self-evaluation (Accessed 2 August 2019).

28   Haylock, D., and Manning, R. (2014). *Mathematics Explained for Primary Teachers*. (5th edn, London: SAGE).

29   Askew, M. (2015). *Transforming Primary Mathematics* (2nd edn, Abingdon: Routledge).

30   Barton, C. (2018). *How I Wish I'd Taught Maths: Lessons Learned from Research, Conversations with Experts, and 12 Years of Mistakes* (Woodbridge: John Catt Educational).

31   Southall, E. (2017). *Yes, But Why? Teaching for Understanding in Mathematics* (London: SAGE).

32   Mattock, P. (2019). *Visible Maths* (Carmarthen: Crown House Publishing).

33   Coe R., Aloisi C., Higgins S., and Major, L. E. (2014). *What Makes Great Teaching? Review of the Underpinning Research* (London: The Sutton Trust).

34   Lemov, D., Woolway, E. and Yezzy, K. (2012). *Practice Perfect*. (San Francisco: Jossey Bass).

35   Meyer, D. (2013). *Hollywood Hates Math*. Available at: https://www.youtube.com/watch?v=3uYBoWH3nFk (Accessed 2 August 2019).

Index

Page numbers in *italics* refer to figures.

for developing reasoning 110–12
procedural variation 73–7
progressive 123
for promoting depth 116–17
quizzing 48–9, 54

reasoning 109–10, *110*
progression in 112–13
questions for developing 110–12
stages of 112
representations 20–1, 30, 84, 121, *121*, 133
identification of 34–6, *35*
links between 35–6
value of 31–4
reteaching 55, 85
retrieval practice 48
review 50, 59–60, *60*, 134
distal 61–4
proximal 61–2
quadrants 63–4
Rosenshine, Barak 11, 62
Rosenthal, R. 6
RUCSAC approach to problem-solving 103–4, *103*
Russell, Susan 95

SATs 1, 49
scaffolding 48, 55, 82, 119 *see also* interventions
and differentiation 119
resources 121
through activity 120–1, *121*
through support 119–20
through time 120
schema 59
school culture 137–8
secondary education 15
setting and streaming 12–14
shapes 40–1, 67–8, *68*
Southall, Ed 128
staff meetings 134
statistics 75

stem sentences 29–30, 80–2
subject associations 128–9
subject knowledge of teachers 15, 16, 127–8
subtraction 74–5, 79, 99
success rate 11, 44, 95
summative assessment 47, 50
surface structure of problems 106
Sweller, J. 18–19

talk 80–1
pupil-to-pupil 81–2
pupil-to-teacher 81
teachers
attitudes of 6
CDP *see* CPD
initial teacher training 16–17
mathematics lead, becoming 127–9
primary mathematics teacher 15–17
pupil-to-teacher talk 81
subject knowledge of 15–16, 127–8
teaching assistants (TAs) 87
test anxiety 49
testing 47, 49–51
three-part lessons 89
trackers 84, 123
Transforming Primary Mathematics (Askew) 128
Trends in International Mathematics and Science Study
(TIMSS) 5
triangles, conceptual variation with 70–1, *71*
Twitter 17, 129

understanding 20 *see also* depth

variation theory 20, 67
Visible Maths (Mattock) 128
vocabulary 29–30, 79–80, 111

worked examples 107–8, 120

Yes, But Why? (Southall) 128